*Getting acquainted*
*with comets*

7

BOOKS BY ROBERT S. RICHARDSON

*Getting Acquainted with Comets*
*Astronomy in Action*
*Exploring Mars*
*The Fascinating World of Astronomy*
*Second Satellite (A junior novel)*

AND WITH W. T. SKILLING

*Sun, Moon and Stars*

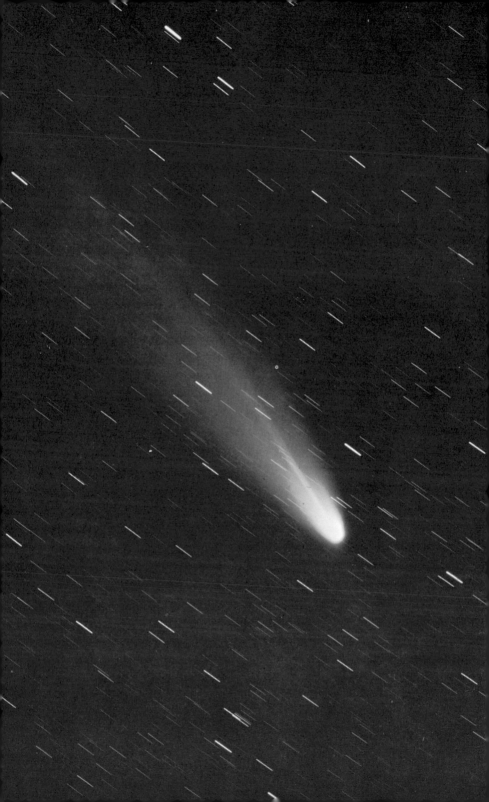

# Getting acquainted with comets

## BY ROBERT S. RICHARDSON

McGRAW-HILL BOOK COMPANY

*New York / Toronto / London / Sydney*

44 258

# Contents

# *Foreword*

This book should not be taken for more than its title implies: some remarks on comets for those who wish to make the acquaintance of these strange objects. No attempt has been made to discuss comets and meteors in detail or to explore the numerous controversial questions connected with them.

Since World War II astronomers in a sense have "discovered" comets and related objects again, gradually awakening to the fact that these bodies within our solar system present just as fascinating material for study as the bodies far outside it. The observation of comets and meteors is one of the few fields remaining in astronomy in which the amateur can still make contributions of value. A spectacular example was the discovery by two amateurs, Kaoru Ikeya and Tsutomu Seki, in September 1965, of a comet which in less than a month developed into one of the brightest that has appeared in nearly a century.

It is hoped that this book may stimulate some to take up comet hunting as a hobby, as well as prove of interest to those who simply wish to know something about comets.

R.S.R., 1966

*Getting acquainted*
*with comets*

# CHAPTER 1

---

## *"How is* your *comet tonight?"*

Your friends press closer as you peer into the eyepiece of the telescope—the telescope you made with your own hands only a few months before. They watch in breathless silence as you give the focusing screw a final touch.

"How is comet Wlodarczyski?" someone cries, unable to restrain his impatience any longer.

You lean back in the observing chair, studying the pale object shining among the stars of Cygnus. "I think the tail is a little longer tonight," you remark, after careful consideration.

An excited murmur runs through the throng. "He says the tail is a little longer tonight!"

You step aside and allow your friends to look through the telescope at the visitor from outer space that bears your name. You become aware of a young lady close beside you, gazing up into your face with awe-struck eyes.

"How wonderful to have a comet of your very own!" she cries. "Tell me, Mr. Wlodarczyski, did you have much trouble finding it?"

"Well, yes and no," you reply. "I was observing the Dumbbell nebula in Vulpecula, when suddenly this fuzzy object attracted my attention. . . ."

It *would* be a wonderful experience to discover a comet, to have it named after you, to read about it in the papers, and to follow its progress across the sky. "But nothing like that could ever happen to *me*," you protest. "How could I ever discover a comet?"

Before you give up without even trying, listen to this true story of how one comet was discovered. It is not an unusual case.

About 8:30 on the evening of July 15, 1931, Mr. Masaji Nagata, of Brawley, California, was examining an object low in the western sky with his 3-inch telescope. (By a "3-inch" is meant a telescope with a lens 3 inches wide in the end of the tube.) During the day he was busy on his farm, but at night he liked to relax by doing a little stargazing. He had begun the evening by turning his telescope on the planet Neptune. Neptune is so far away that in a 3-inch telescope it would be hard to distinguish from a star.

While observing Neptune he noticed a hazy object nearby that he could not recall having seen on the evening before. The next night he picked up the hazy object again, although not in quite the same position. Now the fact that the object looked hazy and had changed position could mean only one thing. It could not be a fixed object in the sky like a nebula or star cluster. It must be a comet! But what do you do with a comet after you've discovered it?

Mr. Nagata had never supposed anything like that could happen to *him*. He knew what to do with a cultivator, or a sack of fertilizer, or a load of melons. But a comet . . . ? He decided to notify the astronomers at the Mount Wilson Observatory some 200 miles to the north.

Now the truth is that people call astronomers about some of the *strangest* things:

"I hear there's a planet been discovered that's square instead of round. Is that right?"

"Say, I'm scared. I've been seeing the moon all day. D'you think it's out of its orbit?"

"Would you please tell me the exact distance of the star in the left hind leg of the Big Bear?"

It is remarkable how many people go crazy about the stars. But a person who really knows something can usually be distinguished from a crank immediately. Nagata's story about his comet must have sounded pretty good, for the night assistant at the 100-inch telescope was assigned the job of checking on the object with a small photographic telescope. Why not the 100-inch telescope? Because in hunting comets you don't want a big telescope, as we shall see later.

That evening the night assistant took a photograph of the sky where Nagata thought his comet should be—and there it was! Right in the middle of the plate.

But that still did not mean Nagata had discovered a new comet. He might have picked up an old comet that had been discovered years before and forgotten about. To check this matter it was necessary to determine the comet's orbit. The first orbit calculated at the Students' Observatory of the University of California at Berkeley showed no resemblance to the orbit of any other known comet.

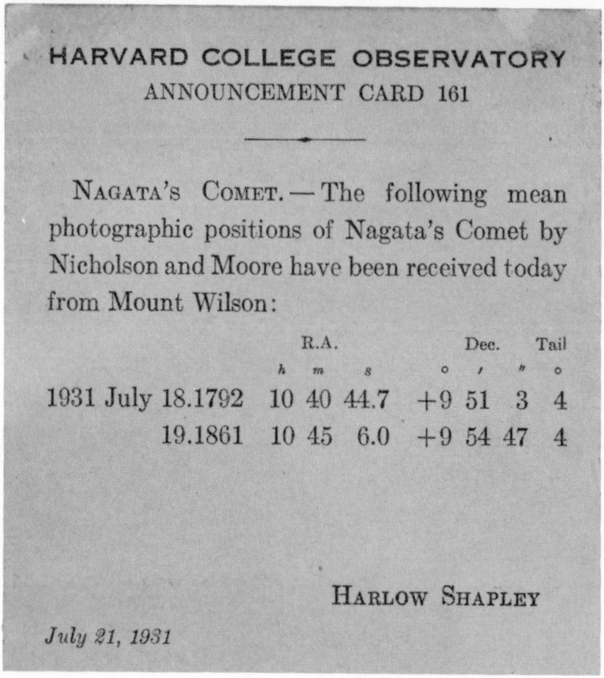

HARVARD COLLEGE OBSERVATORY
ANNOUNCEMENT CARD 161

NAGATA'S COMET. — The following mean photographic positions of Nagata's Comet by Nicholson and Moore have been received today from Mount Wilson:

| | R.A. | | | Dec. | | | Tail |
|---|---|---|---|---|---|---|---|
| | h | m | s | ° | ′ | ″ | ° |
| 1931 July 18.1792 | 10 | 40 | 44.7 | +9 | 51 | 3 | 4 |
| 19.1861 | 10 | 45 | 6.0 | +9 | 54 | 47 | 4 |

HARLOW SHAPLEY

*July 21, 1931*

FIGURE 1. Announcement from the Harvard College Observatory of observations of the comet discovered by Masaji Nagata by astronomers at the Mount Wilson Observatory.

It was therefore a new and unexpected comet, a genuine discovery. (Fig. 1)

Later the Astronomical Society of the Pacific presented Nagata with the Donahoe Comet Medal, an award that used to be made every year to anyone who discovered an unexpected comet. The new comet was officially named "Nagata's comet," and is so known to this day.

Although Nagata's comet never became bright enough to be seen without a telescope, it received considerable publicity because of the way it was discovered. Many people could not understand how the astronomers on Mount Wilson with their big telescopes could have lost such a prize to a humble melon grower with a 3-inch telescope. But astronomers at large observatories seldom make a business of looking for comets. And, as already mentioned, a *big* telescope is the *worst* telescope for finding comets.

Nagata understood the situation and was very grateful for the help the astronomers at Mount Wilson gave him. To show his appreciation he presented them with a crate of melons from his farm.

Nagata died a few years later. But the comet that bears his name is still out there among the stars.

CHAPTER 2

---

# Comets compared with other objects in the sky

We cannot appreciate the extraordinary features about comets unless we first know something about other objects in the sky. (A man from Mars might not be able to appreciate a giraffe at first sight; so far as he knows ALL inhabitants of planet Earth have necks 10 feet long.) So let's take a few moments to talk about planets, asteroids, meteoroids, and the stars.

The first book on astronomy I ever read represented the solar system by a model in which the sun was a pumpkin at the center, and the planets were fruit and vegetables of different sizes. This fruit-and-vegetable solar system has long been a favorite with authors who write popular books on the stars. Anyone who uses it again must be lacking in imagination indeed. But after long thought on the matter I'll admit I cannot think of a better scheme.

To lay out our solar system we need a flat piece of ground about 4 miles square. The ground must be flat because the planets revolve around the sun in orbits that do not lie much above or below one another. You can think of the planets as marbles rolling around on a table top.

We place a pumpkin 30 inches in diameter at the center of the field to represent the sun. (Fig. 2) The sun is by far the largest and most massive body in the solar system. That is why it is called the *solar* system, the word "solar" meaning "of the sun." The sun, because of its great mass, dominates the motion of the planets and other bodies in its vicinity. And it is a solar *system* because the planets move around the sun, not at random, but in a systematic way that can be foretold in advance. We shall represent the orbits of the planets by circles, with the sun at their centers, although actually their paths depart slightly from circular motion. (Fig. 3)

On the scale we have selected, Mercury is a pea 36 yards from the pumpkin. Venus is a pea twice as large at a distance of 67 yards. The earth is another pea of the same size at 93 yards; and 9 inches from it we put a radish seed to represent the moon. Mars is a smaller pea at 142 yards from the pumpkin. Mars has two moons so tiny that it is hard to find anything small enough for them. We represent them by a couple of celery seeds at ¼ and ½ inch from Mars. These four pea-size bodies are often called the "terrestrial" planets, meaning the planets "like the earth." Although Mercury, Venus, and Mars differ from the earth in many ways, they are similar to the earth in being roughly the same size and mass.

We have to go a quarter of a mile from the pumpkin to place an orange to represent Jupiter, the largest planet of the solar system. Jupiter has twelve satellites, four giant

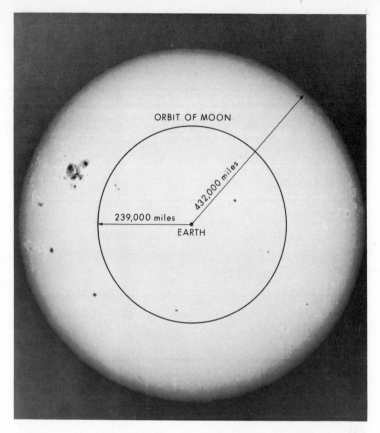

ORBIT OF MOON

432,000 miles

239,000 miles

EARTH

FIGURE 2. Orbit of the moon compared with the size of the sun. The sun is so big that the earth could be put in its center with plenty of room left for the moon to revolve in its present path.

satellites and eight small ones. The four giant satellites are about the size of our moon and revolve at distances of from 10 to 50 inches from Jupiter on our scale. The smaller moons we shall represent by celery seeds again, the nearest being only 4 inches from Jupiter, and the most distant 563 inches, or 16 yards, from the planet. Saturn is a smaller orange distant one-half mile with ten known moons, the biggest moon being about the size of Mercury at 27 inches from our model Saturn, and the other small ones scattered over distances from the planet ranging from 4 inches to 8 yards. Uranus would be a plum distant 1 mile from the central pumpkin, with five small satellites. Neptune would be another plum at 1½ miles. Neptune has one giant satellite probably almost the size of Mars at a distance of 8 inches, the same as the distance of our moon. But Neptune also is known to have a tiny moon revolving at about 124 inches on our scale, or 3.5 yards. Finally we come to the outermost planet, Pluto, which we shall represent by a pea at 2 miles from the pumpkin. Jupiter, Saturn, Uranus, and Neptune are often referred to as the "giant" planets, or the "Jovian" planets after Jupiter, their prototype.

Our model of the solar system is now complete so far as the major planets and their satellites are concerned. How to represent the minor members is a problem. (Fig. 3)

## THE ASTEROIDS

Revolving, with only a few exceptions, between the orbits of Mars and Jupiter are a host of tiny bodies, whose total mass is hardly 1/1000 that of the earth. There are now nearly 2000 that have been named and numbered and had their orbits computed. The total number within range of the 100-inch telescope has been conservatively estimated at 44,000. The largest of these asteroids is Ceres, about 450 miles in diameter. The smallest that can be observed are about 1 mile in diameter. To include them in our model solar system, we scatter celery seeds about 300 yards from the pumpkin, between the orbits of Mars and Jupiter.

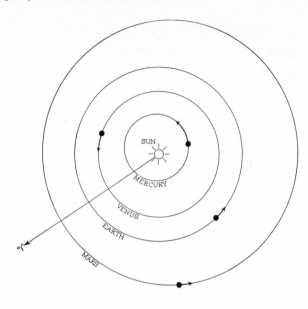

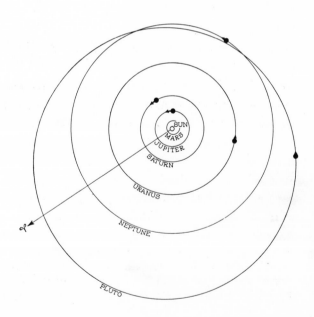

There are so many asteroids and they are so much alike that astronomers don't try to discover them any more. Actually, it is almost impossible for astronomers *not* to discover an asteroid. Often on their photographs they will find an asteroid or two as a matter of accident. The stars, being fixed in the sky, appear as round images on the plate. But since an asteroid is moving, it shows on the plate as an elongated image which often can be recognized at once.

If the trail is unusually long, it is worth taking enough plates to enable computers to get the orbit of the asteroid. For its rapid motion indicates it is one of the unusual "male" asteroids which move in elongated paths that cross the orbit of the earth. The orbit of the asteroid Icarus extends from beyond the orbit of Mars to within the orbit of Mercury. The farthest-ranging asteroid is Hidalgo, whose orbit reaches out to Saturn.

## METEOROIDS, METEORITES, AND METEORS

Bodies too small to be detected by the largest telescopes may be considered as meteoroids. A meteoroid may be anywhere in space. It need have no connection with the

FIGURE 3. The planets are spread over such a great range of distance that it is difficult to show their orbits to scale in the same diagram. Here their orbits are shown on two diagrams drawn to different scales, but with the orbit of Mars common to both. The mean distance of Mars from the sun is 142 million miles. Arrows attached to planets indicate their velocities. The orbital velocity of the earth is 18.5 miles per second.

earth. Occasionally a meteoroid encounters the earth, however, and rushes into our atmosphere. It strikes the air particles with such high velocity that it soon becomes surrounded by a cloud of glowing gas. This *light* that we see in the sky is a meteor. It is *not* the body itself. You cannot contact a meteor any more than you can contact the noise of the wind. If the meteoroid is large enough to survive its fiery plunge through the atmosphere and reach the surface of the earth, we call it a *meteorite*.

*Micrometeorites* are such tiny particles that they melt in flight and lose most of their velocity before reaching the earth's surface. But what they lack in size they make up in abundance, for they constitute most of the material that reaches us from outer space.

COSMIC DUST

If we only become aware of a meteoroid by the momentary streak of light it leaves in the sky as a "shooting star," what chance do we have of seeing still smaller particles millions of miles away? Such particles are hopelessly beyond any method of detection individually, but they are not particularly difficult to observe collectively. On some clear moonless night in March or April, when you are far from artificial lights, keep watch on the western horizon for several evenings. Just before the stars appear you may be rewarded by the sight of a ghostly column of light extending into the twilight sky. This is the *zodiacal light*. It arises from a cloud of dust particles revolving around the sun in the plane of the earth's orbit, and probably far beyond it. The zodiacal light is one of those things you have to see in order to believe. Only once have I gotten a good view of it, from the Lick Observatory on Mount Hamilton, Cailfornia. I have often seen it from Mount Wilson in the morning as a glow in the eastern sky as if the moon were about to rise.

There is still another ghostly glow in the sky which few people have seen or even heard about. This is the *gegenschein,* from the German word meaning "counterglow," since it is always opposite or "counter" in position to the sun. The gegenschein is a good object for amateur observers, as it is visible ONLY to the unaided eye, being much too large and diffuse to be seen in a telescope. The nature of the gegenschein is still uncertain. It may be a kind of gaseous tail formed by particles from the atmosphere streaming into space away from the earth in the opposite direction from the sun.

## WHERE ARE THE STARS IN OUR MODEL?

In our model of the solar system we put Pluto, the outermost planet, 2 miles from the sun, represented by a pumpkin. Where would the nearest star be on this scale? Suppose our solar system were laid out in the state of Kansas. Just at a guess you might put the nearest star several hundred miles away, in Nebraska or Colorado. But that would be much too close. How about moving it down to Mexico or somewhere up in Canada? No, we are still much too close. On the scale of our model, the nearest star, Alpha Centauri, would be 14,000 miles from the central pumpkin. And the luminous blue-white star Rigel in the constellation of Orion would be about ten times as far away as the moon! (Fig. 4)

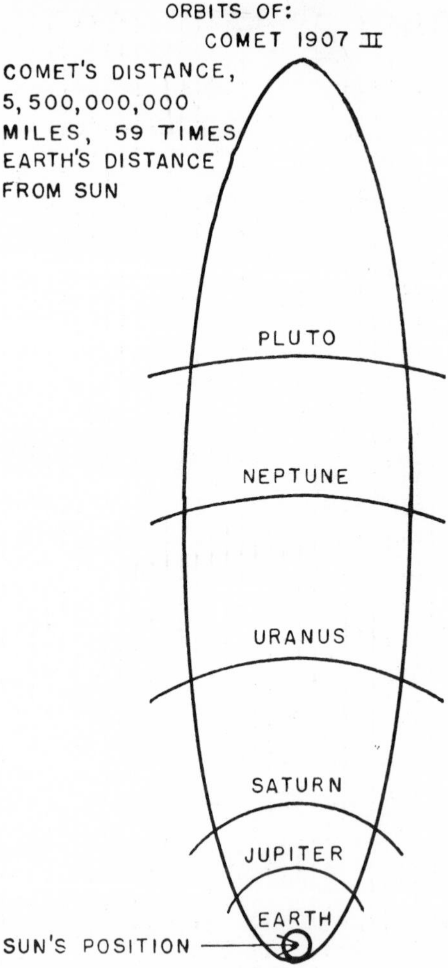

ORBITS OF:

COMET 1907 II

COMET'S DISTANCE,
5,500,000,000
MILES, 59 TIMES
EARTH'S DISTANCE
FROM SUN

PLUTO

NEPTUNE

URANUS

SATURN

JUPITER

EARTH

SUN'S POSITION

FIGURE 4.   Comet 1907 II has an orbit that extends 5.5 billion miles from the sun, far beyond the boundary of the outermost known planet, Pluto. The lines drawn back and forth (*right*) show how many times the orbit of Comet 1907 II would stretch out to reach to the nearest star, Alpha Centauri, distant 26 trillion miles (4.3 light years). (Griffith Observatory, Los Angeles.)

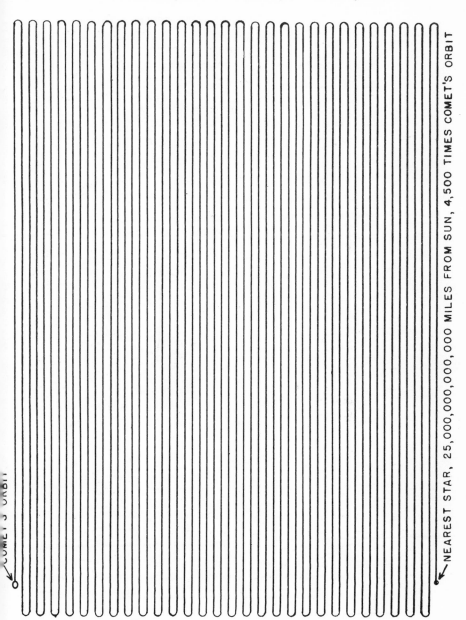

COMET'S ORBIT

NEAREST STAR, 25,000,000,000,000 MILES FROM SUN, 4,500 TIMES COMET'S ORBIT

WHAT KIND OF BODIES ARE THE PLANETS?

Returning to the solar system, what sort of bodies are its major members, the planets?

Except for their atmospheric shells, you can think of the planets as hard, cold bodies with a solid surface, like marbles of different sizes made of various substances. The earth is a small marble made of some heavy substance like a ball bearing. Jupiter corresponds to a much larger marble made of a lighter substance such as plastic. Yet Jupiter is 318 times as massive as the earth. The reason is evident from Tables 1 and 2. In Table 1 the planets are listed in order of increasing *size*. We see this is also the order in

T A B L E   1

Size and mass of the planets

| Planet | Diameter (Earth = 1) | Diameter (miles) | Mass (Earth = 1) |
|---|---|---|---|
| Moon | 0.272 | 2,160 | 0.0123 |
| Mercury | 0.365 | 2,896 | 0.054 |
| Mars | 0.535 | 4,244 | 0.108 |
| Venus | 0.956 | 7,581 | 0.817 |
| Earth | 1.000 | 7,926 | 1.000 |
| Uranus | 3.896 | 30,880 | 14.6 |
| Neptune | 3.920 | 31,070 | 17.1 |
| Saturn | 9.486 | 75,190 | 95.0 |
| Jupiter | 11.190 | 88,700 | 317.4 |

which they increase in *mass*. The reason Jupiter is so much more massive than the earth is plain enough: there is so MUCH MORE of Jupiter than there is of the earth. (Fig. 5)

Table 2 shows how the planets would increase in mass if they were all the *same* size. We see that the order is quite different from that in Table 1. Thus, volume for volume—pint for pint or bushel for bushel—there is much more material in the earth and Mercury than in Saturn or any of the other Jovian planets. The figures in Table 2 are averages for the whole planet. Their masses are much more concentrated in their deep interiors than at their surfaces.

Table 2 shows that a representative sample of Uranus

# T A B L E  2

## Mass of the planets if all were the same size

| Planet | Mass (Earth = 1) | Mass (Water = 1) |
|---|---|---|
| Saturn | 0.13 | 0.72 |
| Uranus | 0.25 | 1.36 |
| Jupiter | 0.25 | 1.38 |
| Neptune | 0.28 | 1.56 |
| Moon | 0.61 | 3.35 |
| Mars | 0.70 | 3.87 |
| Venus | 0.93 | 5.15 |
| Earth | 1.00 | 5.52 |
| Mercury | 1.11 | 6.17 |

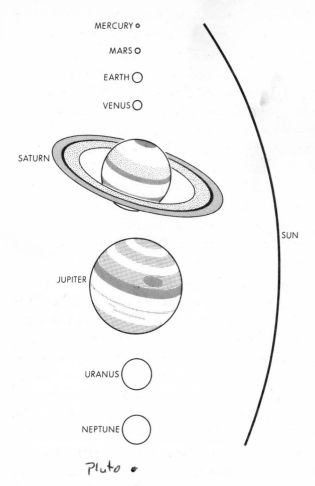

Pluto ●

FIGURE 5. Comparative sizes of the sun and planets. The diameter of the sun is 865,000 miles. Jupiter, the largest planet, is 86,000 miles in diameter; the earth has an equatorial diameter of 7927 miles.

and Jupiter would only weigh one-fourth as much as a representative sample of the same size of the earth. In fact, the only planet that outweighs the earth volume for volume is Mercury. (Older measures make Mercury somewhat lighter.) The third column shows how a representative sample of the planets compares in weight with the same size volume of water. Saturn is composed of such lightweight stuff that theoretically it would float in water. The other planets are all heavier than water, although Jupiter and Uranus by only about 37 per cent. The Jovian planets probably consist almost entirely of the lightest elements, hydrogen and helium, in solid form. The terrestrial planets evidently contain large amounts of heavy metallic elements such as iron.

The stars are huge bodies similar to the sun but so far away that they have shrunk to mere points of light. Even when seen through the largest telescopes, a star still appears essentially the same as it does to your eye: a bright, sparkling point of light. No amount of magnification will make a star show a disk as the sun does. We know of stars that are thousands of times more luminous than the sun. We also know of a star that is a million times fainter. The stars are self-luminous bodies that shine because of the energy released deep inside them from nuclear reactions. The planets are much smaller than the stars you see at night and emit no light of their own. We see the moon and planets only because of the light they reflect to us from the sun. If the sun went out, the moon and planets would, too. But the stars would continue shining just as usual. The stars, of course, have nothing to do with our little solar system.

FIGURE 6. The planet Venus is about the same size as the earth. It is always cloud-covered so that we know little about the planet's solid surface. The cloud layer rarely shows markings when viewed by the eye. In this photograph taken in ultraviolet light, cloud markings are clearly visible. (60-inch telescope, Mount Wilson and Palomar Observatories. Enlarged reproduction by Griffith Observatory.)

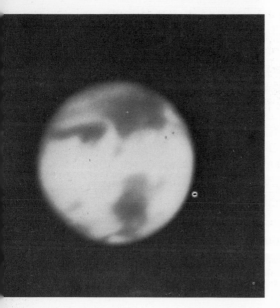

FIGURE 7. Mars is a planet about half the diameter of the earth. The dark markings on the disk appear bluish-gray when viewed with a reflecting telescope. White areas are light orange or reddish brown. Because the dark bluish-gray markings change tint with the Martian seasons, some observers believe they may be covered by vegetation. The craters on Mars revealed by Mariner IV are much too small to show on this photograph taken with the 200-inch telescope. (Mount Wilson and Palomar Observatories.)

FIGURE 8. Jupiter, the largest planet, is always covered by clouds which show a banded structure. The clouds are continually changing, indicating violent disturbances of an unknown nature beneath their surface. (Photographed in blue light with 100-inch telescope, Mount Wilson and Palomar Observatories.)

FIGURE 9. Saturn, the second-largest planet, is unique among the planets in possessing a ring. The interior of Saturn is probably similar in constitution to Jupiter. (Photograph by 100-inch telescope, Mount Wilson and Palomar Observatories.)

Where do the comets belong in the solar system. Or *do* they belong in the solar system? The comets are huge, diffuse objects quite different from the hard, solid planets. The zodiacal light reminds us a little of comets. But the particles in the zodiacal light emit no light themselves; they shine entirely by reflected light, the same as the planets. But the light of comets differs in many ways from reflected sunlight. Is it possible that they emit some light of their own? When it comes to size, comets are immense, some of them occupying a volume of space larger than the sun. But what about their mass? Are they as massive as Neptune, or earth, or even the moon? Are comets made of the same common substances found in the earth and in our own bodies? Or are they made of alien substances wholly unknown to us?

These are a few of the questions we shall try to answer in the pages that follow.

# CHAPTER 3

---

# *What is a comet?*

Trying to describe a "typical" comet is like trying to describe a "typical" woman's hat. About the best you can hope to do is to strike a general average.

Most of the people who read this have probably never seen a comet. Yet comets are not at all rare objects. On any night there are usually three or four somewhere in the sky. But you need a telescope to see them. Comets visible to the unaided eye *are* rare objects. And spectacularly bright comets are such rare objects that you would have to be very lucky to see two or three in a lifetime. To become a bright naked-eye object, a comet has to satisfy at least four conditions:

1. It must be a big comet.

2. It must come close enough to the sun to be excited to high luminosity.

3. While near the sun, it must also be near the earth.

4. When near the sun and earth, it must be in the night sky. (Although there have been a few comets so bright that they were visible in the *day* sky.)

Very seldom does a comet satisfy all four conditions simultaneously. It is not surprising, therefore, that when a bright comet does suddenly blaze forth people regard it with wonder and dread. What is it? Where did it come from? What does it MEAN?

Always, people suppose a comet to be a portent of evil rather than good. (Probably a subconscious wish to project their own sins onto some other body.) The hairy star is regarded as a warning to mankind foretelling war, famine, and the death of kings. Since history is filled with such events, it is easy enough to find considerable support for such hypotheses. The sinister aspect of a comet acts as a powerful stimulus to the imagination. In 1528 a bright comet threw the population of Europe into a panic. Ambrose Paré, a noted surgeon of that time, has left us this account of its appearance:

"The comet was so horrible and frightful, and produced such great terror among the populace, that some died of fear and others fell sick. It appeared as a star of excessive length and the color of blood; at its summit was seen the figure of a bent arm holding a great sword in its hand, as if about to strike. At this point there were three stars. On both sides of the rays of this comet were seen a great number of axes, knives, and spaces colored with blood, among which were a great number of hideous human faces with beards and bristling hair."

What a comfort Dr. Paré must have been to his patients in the operating room!

## DEVELOPMENT OF A COMET

Few comets become bright enough to be observable with a telescope until about midway between the orbits of Jupiter and Mars, corresponding to a distance from the sun of 279,000,000 miles, or 3 AU (Hereafter, instead of giving distances in miles followed by long strings of zeros, we shall give them in terms of the *astronomical unit*, AU—the AU being the distance between the earth and sun, 93 million miles). Today a comet is generally discovered by photography rather than by the eye. On the discovery photograph the comet appears as an unstupendous point of light with perhaps a little haze around it, scarcely distinguishable from the star images. In fact, often astronomers are doubtful whether they have picked up a comet or an asteroid, and to be on the safe side they prefer to call it simply an "object." But if later observations show the object is moving in an elongated orbit, and if the haze around it becomes brighter, then we are pretty safe in upgrading the "object" to a "comet." On the other hand, if the orbit turns out to be only slightly elongated, and if the object continues to present a starlike appearance, it is *probably* an asteroid. But as we shall see, it is still possible to be mistaken. (Fig. 10)

For several weeks after discovery, the comet is hardly more than a mathematical abstraction, a mere geometrical point in space moving in accordance with the law of gravitation. As the comet nears the sun, however, it becomes of interest as a *physical body*. Now the nebulosity around the nucleus, barely visible before, begins to expand and brighten under the increasing intensity of the sun's rays, forming the *coma*. (Fig. 11)

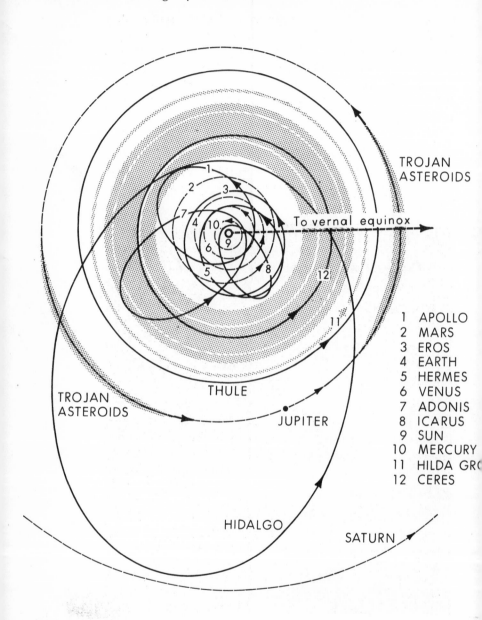

TROJAN
ASTEROIDS

To vernal equinox

TROJAN
ASTEROIDS

THULE

JUPITER

| | |
|---|---|
| 1 | APOLLO |
| 2 | MARS |
| 3 | EROS |
| 4 | EARTH |
| 5 | HERMES |
| 6 | VENUS |
| 7 | ADONIS |
| 8 | ICARUS |
| 9 | SUN |
| 10 | MERCURY |
| 11 | HILDA GR( |
| 12 | CERES |

HIDALGO

SATURN

FIGURE 10. *Left.* Most asteroids revolve in approximately circular orbits between Mars and Jupiter. But a few, such as Icarus, Adonis, Hidalgo, and others, revolve in elongated orbits similar to the short-period comets. Such asteroids are difficult to distinguish from comets. (From "The Discovery of Icarus" by Robert S. Richardson, *Scientific American,* April 1965.)

FIGURE 11. *Below.* A drawing illustrating the general appearance of a comet, showing nucleus, coma, and a portion of the tail. (Ray Benton, Melpar, Inc. Illustration by George D. Schwald, Sept. 1963.)

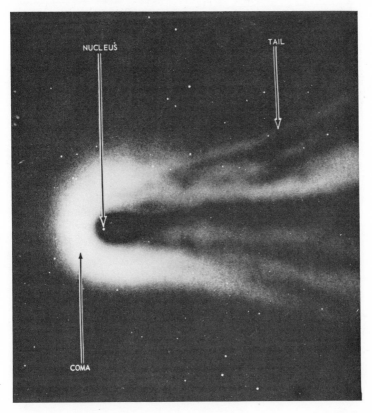

So far the comet has lacked that appendage which is popularly regarded as the prime essential of a comet—its *tail*. But few comets begin to develop a tail until within about 1.6 AU of the sun, at the distance of the orbit of Mars. Whether a comet develops much of a tail or not depends upon how close it is destined to come to the sun. There are comets known as "sun grazers" that have passed through the solar atmosphere within less than a million miles of the surface of the sun itself. Such comets often have tails of enormous length, long enough to span the distance between the sun and earth. Of course, it is not easy to say exactly where such a filmy thing as the tail of a comet "ends," so that the lengths recorded for some of them are not very reliable. The record for tail length still seems to be held by the great comet of 1843, which passed within a half million miles of the sun's surface. Its tail appeared to reach a third of the way across the sky, and in actual length was estimated at 200 million miles, or twice the distance between earth and sun.

It is easy to be mistaken about the length of a comet's tail. A comet that appears to have a tail that is hardly worth mentioning may actually have a very long one. It all depends upon our point of view. If the comet's tail is situated in space so that we see it end-on, then the comet will appear to be all nucleus and coma even if its tail stretches across a couple of astronomical units. It is when we see the tail side-on, so that its full length is exposed to our view, that it appears to best advantage. There have been cases when a comet appeared to have an *anti-tail*, or a tail pointing in the opposite direction from its main tail. (Figs. 12 & 13)

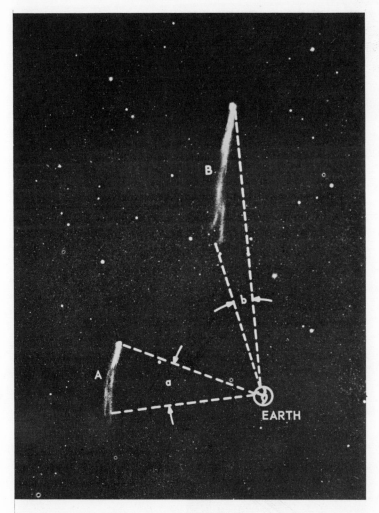

FIGURE 12. The apparent length of a comet's tail is very deceptive, as its extent depends upon how we see it. Although Comet B actually has a longer tail than Comet A, its tail appears shorter as viewed from the earth. (Ray Benton, Melpar, Inc. Drawing by George D. Schwald, Sept. 1963.)

FIGURE 13. *Left.* Comet Arend-Roland photographed on April 25, 1957, showing spike or "anti-tail" projecting from head. The anti-tail was an effect due to perspective and does not contradict the statement that a comet's tail always points away from the sun. (Lick Observatory, Mount Hamilton, California.)

FIGURE 14. *Right.* The changing orientation of a comet's tail as it swings around the sun at the perihelion of its orbit. The tail always points in nearly the opposite direction from the sun. (Ray Benton, Melpar, Inc. Drawing by George D. Schwald, Sept. 1963.)

## WHICH WAY DOES THE TAIL POINT?

The answer to this question may seem obvious to you at first glance. The tail of a comet, you might want to answer, sticks out behind it, of course, in the opposite direction to its motion. After all, a flaming pine knot hurled through the air leaves a "tail" behind it formed by the resistance of the air to the flimsy smoke particles. Upon more careful investigation, however, we begin to wonder whether the smoke trails we see around us on the earth have any analogy whatever with a comet's tail. Terrestrial smoke trails may have any direction, depending upon which way the wind is blowing, or the direction of motion of their source.

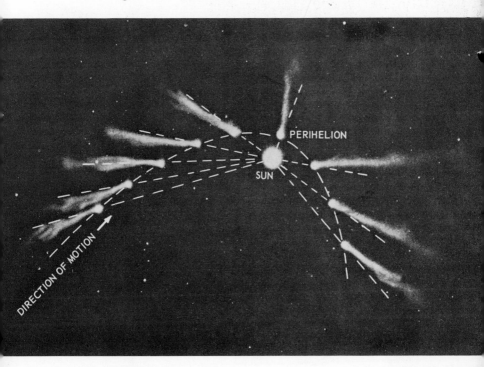

But, regardless of which way a comet is moving, the tail of a comet *always* points *away from the sun*. If the tail is a long one, it is usually curved slightly, the end lagging behind the nucleus as if the material were being blown back by a strong headwind. Although the tail occupies an immense volume in space, the material within it is in such an extremely rarefied condition that the total mass is insignificant. Often we see stars shining through the tail without their light being dimmed in the slightest.

### WHY AWAY FROM THE SUN?

Why *should* the tail of a comet always point away from the sun? Some three centuries ago Johannes Kepler speculated that the particles in the tail were driven from the nucleus by a repulsive force emanating from the sun. What was this repulsive force? Previous to about 1930 astronomers thought they knew the answer—light pressure. That light exerts a pressure was demonstrated theoretically by the great British physicist James Clerk Maxwell about the middle of the last century, and detected experimentally in 1900 by the Russian physicist Pëtr Nikolaevich Lebedev. The pressure exerted by sunlight on a square foot of surface is pretty small, about 1/10,000,000 of a pound. But inside the sun, where the temperature is measured in millions of degrees, the pressure of radiation builds up to many million times the pressure of our atmosphere. Even far outside the sun, space travel under suitable conditions might be carried on by means of "solar sailing"; that is, by utilizing the pressure of sunlight falling upon a sail of immense area but very small mass. And early in this century it seemed reasonable to suppose that in outer space particles were repelled from the head of a comet to form its tail.

A particle in the solar system is acted upon by two forces. One is the force of gravitation, always directed toward the sun. The other is a repulsive force due to solar radiation directed always away from the sun. The force of gravitation depends upon the *mass* of the particle. Radiation pressure depends upon its size, or, more accurately, upon the area exposed to the sun's rays. For a particle 6/100,000 of an inch in diameter, radiation pressure and gravitational attraction are equal. If the particles are smaller than this critical size, radiation pressure predominates. Radiation pressure continues to increase as the particles become smaller, until at a diameter of 1/100,000 of an inch it exceeds gravitation tenfold. It does not increase indefinitely with decreasing size, however, but reaches its greatest value for solid particles at about one-third the wave-length of the light waves striking it. To fix the idea in mind, you might think of the steady flow of solar radiation as a vast wind rushing through space, sweeping the smaller particles before it but having little effect upon the larger ones. (But the analogy is an imperfect one that is useful only as an aid to the memory.)

The hypothesis of a comet's tail formed by the repulsive force of radiation was advanced about the beginning of this century and was accepted practically without question for thirty years. Within the last two decades it has fallen into disfavor, as the pressure of radiation is much too small to explain the long, straight tails observed on so many comets. Recently, the repulsive force has been attributed to charged particles ejected from the sun with high velocity, but this idea also encounters serious difficulties. At present, there is no satisfactory answer to the question of why a comet's tail always points away from the sun.

## THE NUCLEUS

The material that forms the coma and tail of a comet *must* come from *some*place, the most likely place being the nucleus. It seems safe to conclude that if there were no nucleus there would be no comet. (Some comets show no well-marked nucleus.) Hence the nature of the nucleus is of paramount interest.

Cosmically speaking, the mass of the nucleus is very small. But how much is "very small"? Does it mean the nucleus is no more massive than the earth, or the moon, or even one of the large asteroids?

We measure the mass of a body by its disturbing attraction upon some other body. The difficulty is that if the body is very small its disturbing effect on another body is insignificant, unless the two happen to make an exceptionally close approach. An example occurs in the case of our moon, which is 239,000 miles, or a mere 0.0026 AU, away from us. So far as is known, no other objects larger than meteoroids have ever approached this close.* We think of the earth as revolving around the sun, and the moon as revolving around the earth. Isn't the orbit of the moon always shown as a circle drawn around the earth? It is true that this is the approximate form of the moon's orbit when

---

* The closest known approach of an asteroid is that of Hermes, which came within 485,000 miles on October 30, 1937.

referred to *us*. But since the moon accompanies the earth wherever it goes, the moon must of necessity also revolve around the sun. If you tried to draw the paths of the earth and moon accurately to scale referred to the *sun,* you would find they are so closely intertwined as to be almost indistinguishable. *Both* moon and earth would appear to be revolving around the sun in circles.

If a small portion of their paths, covering about a month, were drawn on a very large scale, however, you would see that the moon's path around the sun has a slight wavy motion. That is, the moon revolves around the sun but its motion is slightly disturbed by the attraction of the earth. If the scale of the diagram were large enough, you would also detect a slight wavy effect in the path of the earth. For the moon also disturbs the motion of the earth, but only to a small degree, owing to its lesser mass. Nevertheless, the disturbance is accurately measurable and serves to determine the mass of the moon as 1/81 of the earth's mass. Even if the moon were somehow invisible, it could never escape detection, as its presence would be immediately revealed by its disturbing effect on the earth.

In theory, therefore, the mass of a comet can be found in the same way: by its disturbing effect on some nearby body. We know of several close encounters. Comet Brooks II passed inside the orbit of the fifth satellite of Jupiter (J V), missing the planet's surface by only 55,000 miles. As if in punishment for its impudent behavior, Jupiter shortened the comet's period of revolution by twenty-four years. But there was no reciprocal reaction: neither Jupiter nor its satellites were affected in the slightest degree.

The record for a close approach of a comet to the earth

was established some 200 years ago by Lexell's comet, which on July 1, 1770, came within 1,400,000 miles. Its head was swollen to five times the apparent size of the moon. No comet before or since has ever loomed so large in the sky. If a body with the mass of the earth had come that close, it would have increased the length of the year by 2 hours 47 minutes. But there was no evidence that Lexell's comet changed the length of the year by so much as a single second. This information is valuable in a negative sense, in that it tells us the mass of the comet could not have been as much as 1/5000 that of the earth.

Since gravitational methods of determining mass are useless on comets, astronomers have been compelled to resort to various indirect means. One of these is based upon considerations involving the rate at which dust particles are lost from the tail. It gives a value of one-billionth the mass of the earth for Comet Arend-Roland (1957 III) and Comet Mrkos (1957 V). One-billionth of anything sounds pretty small until you convert it into familiar terms. A body one-billionth the mass of the earth would have a mass of 6.6 trillion tons. If such a body consisted entirely of water, it would be 14 miles in diameter, corresponding to a moderate-size asteroid.

The precise value of the mass of the nucleus is not nearly so important as a knowledge of how that mass is distributed through the nucleus. Is it all in one big chunk? Or a few large chunks? Or many small fragments? Or some form that never occurred to us?

# CHAPTER 4

# How comets are named

As we mentioned in Chapter 1, you may experience the thrill of discovering a comet, only to find it is Plunckett's old comet of 1867 that's been lost for half a century. Through the years a comet often acquires so many names that remembering them all is worse than trying to keep track of the characters in a Russian novel. But with care and patience it can be done.

Comets at discovery are often so faint that the safest policy is to refer to them by the nondescript title of "object." Should the "object" prove to be a comet, it is temporarily designated a, b, c, . . ., following the year of its discovery, in addition to the name of the discoverer. For example, a faint comet discovered on January 2, 1963, by Ikeya at Tokyo became Comet Ikeya (1963a); the second comet of that year, discovered on March 19 by Alcock, was designated Comet Alcock (1963b), etc. Competition is so keen that often several observers will spot a new comet on the same night. In that event, two or three names are attached to it, but never more than three. It seems to help in comet hunting if you have an unpronounceable name, as witness Comet Pajdušáková (1953h), Comet Tcherepashtshuk (1956d), Comet Grigg-Skjellerup (1956i), Comet Väisälä (1959 I), and Comet Honda-Mrkos-Pajdušáková. But if your name is Smith or Brown, do not despair. Comets have also been discovered by observers named Johnson, Candy, and Wilson.

Comets are given a permanent designation by the order in which they pass their perihelion, perihelion being the point on their orbit nearest the sun. Usually, this cannot be done for several months or even years after discovery, until their orbits are accurately known. Comet Peltier (1936a), although the first comet discovered in 1936, was the second to pass perihelion that year, as signified later by its designation 1936 II. Since the name of the discoverer is retained, its full title is Comet Peltier (1936 II). If a comet returns periodically at fairly short intervals, say about 200 years or less, the fact is denoted by the prefix P, as P/Oterma, P/Herschel-Rigollet, etc. Notice that there is no need to put "comet" before the name in such cases.

The number of comets discovered by an observer, or team of observers, is shown by an Arabic number after the name. Thus the complete designation for a certain famous comet we shall hear more about is 1925 II P/Schwassmann-Wachmann 1. This would be decoded as follows: 1925 II signifies that it was the second comet to pass the perihelion of its orbit in 1925; the P tells us it is a periodic comet; and the last part means it is the first periodic comet discovered by the astronomers Schwassmann and Wachmann. Just to keep the situation from becoming too simple, 1925 II later was unknowingly rediscovered and named three more times under the aliases of 1937e, 1939f, and 1941f. The same team has discovered another comet, Schwassmann-Wachmann 2, which is always getting mixed up with their first one, 1925 II.

In the last century it was customary to refer to a particularly bright object as the "great" comet of the year in which it appeared. This system also led to confusion and chaos. The proper name for the "great comet of 1882" is 1882 II (except that it was originally called 1882 III!). Evidently some other comet passed perihelion about the same time.

Although comets are usually named after their discoverer (or discoverers), there are some notable exceptions. Most famous is Halley's comet, which was named after Edmund Halley (1656–1742)—not because he discovered it, but because he correctly predicted its return in 1759. Another famous case is the comet discovered in 1818 by Jean Louis Pons, of the observatory at Marseilles. Johannes Encke found the comet was moving in an orbit so nearly identical with those of comets observed in 1795 and 1805 that he became convinced the three must be one and the same object, with the remarkably short period of 3.3 years. His prediction for the time of its return in 1822 proved so accurate that forever afterward astronomers—with one exception—have called it "Encke's comet." The single exception was Encke himself, who always referred to it as "Pons' comet." Although Encke devoted about forty years of his life to keeping track of this comet, apparently he never took the trouble to look at it through a telescope. A desk man to the end!

# CHAPTER 5

---

# *The art of catching a comet*

Nagata was not looking for a comet when he found one. Its discovery was purely an accident. Afterwards, he did everything wrong so far as establishing title to the object was concerned. What he should have done will be discussed in the next chapter. There are certain astronomers over the world, mostly amateurs, who go about searching for comets systematically and who have become very expert at it indeed. What do you need to get into this select group?

First we might mention some of the things you do *not* need. You do not need a license from the government or a degree from a university. You don't need to fill out a questionnaire. You don't need to pass any examination. What you *do* need is a powerful and persistent desire to discover comets. You will need plenty of enthusiasm to keep looking for night after night of fruitless search. You don't have to do it. You will not become an object of scorn and derision if you give up on the job. But one thing is sure: You will never discover a comet by NOT looking for it.

Although some comets have been discovered by the unaided eye, your prospects for finding one without telescopic aid are pretty slim. If a new comet is bright enough to be visible without a telescope, you can be quite sure that by the time you have seen it, a dozen other people will probably have seen it too. When the names of so many people are involved, the chances are the comet will not bear the names of any of them. For example, a spectacularly bright comet appeared unexpectedly in January 1910, that was first seen by some laborers working on a railroad in South Africa. But so many others saw it about the same time that all their claims were rejected and the comet was simply designated 1910 I, the name by which it is known today.

YOUR COMET SEEKER

Even a telescope like Nagata's 3-inch increases your chance of finding a comet so tremendously that the small investment required is recommended if you want to go in for comet hunting in a serious way. If money is of no concern, you can set yourself up in business very quickly. You should be able to get a good 6-inch refractor, equatorially mounted with driving clock, for around $3000. But if you are a novice, you would be wise not to plunge on the first instrument you see. By taking your time you should be able to pick up a good telescope for not more than $200, or possibly only $50. After acquiring some observing experience with a cheap instrument, you are in a better position to go ahead in a more ambitious way.

Before investing in any telescope, a novice would do well to get an expert to examine it first. Don't call up the director of a big observatory and ask his opinion on the 50-power telescopes the Bon Marché is advertising this week. Some amateur can give you much better advice. You can meet such people by joining one of the numerous amateur astronomical societies in your vicinity. Ask a planetarium for the name and address of the secretary of some local organization. Attend their meetings and talk things over with the members in the doughnut-and-coffee session afterward. Beside knowing all the traps and pitfalls in the small-telescope business, they may be able to put you in touch with someone who has a good telescope for sale cheap. Remember that a "good" secondhand telescope is not in the same category as a "good" secondhand car. The optics of a telescope do not deteriorate with age as a car does. One of the best astronomical telescopes in the world today has been in use on every clear night for more than half a century. Do not scorn a telescope because of its tarnished tube and wobbly mounting. These are drawbacks easily corrected. Again—it is the optics of the instrument that count.

REFRACTOR OR REFLECTOR?

There are people who are burning up to get launched on their career of astronomical discovery who are not even aware of the fact that there are two distinct kinds of astronomical telescopes. The only kind of telescope most people

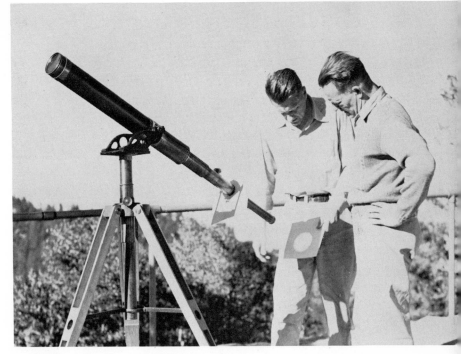

FIGURE 15. A 3-inch refracting (lens) type of telescope similar to Nagata's. The telescope is being used here to examine an enlarged image of the sun.

know about is the kind with a lens in the outer end, or a "refractor." It is called a *refractor* because it refracts, or bends, the light rays to a focus where the image is formed. At the other end is an eyepiece which magnifies the image. By the *aperture* of a telescope is meant the diameter of the lens in the outer end, or *objective*. Nagata's refractor, for example, had an objective of 3 inches aperture. (Fig. 15)

Remove the eyepiece and point the telescope at a bright object such as the moon. Hold a card at the position of the eyepiece. You will find a bright spot on the card, formed by the rays of the moon. By moving the card back and forth, you can locate the *focus* of the objective lens where the image of the moon comes out sharp and clear. The distance from the objective to the image is the *focal length* of the lens. In astronomy or photography or any kind of optical observing, it is highly essential to know how the focal length of your instrument compares with its aperture, or its *focal ratio*. If the focal length of your objective lens is 30 inches, and its aperture 3 inches, then its focal ratio is $30/3 = 10$. It is customary to express the focal ratio by its "F-number"; for example, the 3-inch lens just mentioned would have a focal ratio of F/10. If its focal length were 60 inches, its focal ratio would be F/20. The larger the focal ratio of a lens, the larger is the image it gives. A lens of 60 inches focal length gives an image twice the size of a lens of focal length 30 inches. But although the image is larger it is also fainter, since the same amount of light is spread over a larger surface. The focal ratio that an astronomer chooses for his telescope will depend upon the type of work he wants to do with it. If he intends to use it chiefly on bright objects like the moon and planets, a telescope of long focal length will be of advantage—say, one with a focal ratio of F/15 or F/20. (The sun is so bright you can use a focal ratio of around F/200!) But if he is after faint extended objects such as nebulae and comets, he has to sacrifice size of image to brightness of image, and use a focal ratio of around F/3.

Astronomers use a simpler type of eyepiece than the ordinary or "terrestrial" type used for looking at objects on the earth. If you looked at objects with an astronomical eyepiece, they would all appear upside down. To show them erect you must insert more lenses in the eyepiece.

But there is no upside down or right side up in the
heavens. A comet looks just as good one way as the other.
Also, the fewer lenses in your optical system the better.
Lenses absorb and scatter light, and hence make the image
fainter and less distinct. You soon become accustomed to
an astronomical eyepiece and after a while would find a
right-side-up eyepiece confusing.

Beginners are always impressed by the degree of magnification or "power" of a telescope, 50 power or 100 power,
whatever it may be. The magnifying power of a telescope
depends upon the focal length of the objective divided by
the focal length of the eyepiece. If you have an objective
of 50 inches focal length, and an eyepiece of 1-inch focal
length, the magnifying power secured is 50/1 = 50. By inserting an eyepiece of ½-inch focal length the magnification would be 50/½ = 100. Thus you can get almost any
magnification you want by using an eyepiece of sufficiently
short focal length. Now the expensive part of a telescope is
the objective; eyepieces are comparatively cheap. Astronomical telescopes are usually equipped with a battery of
half a dozen eyepieces of various focal lengths, giving a
wide range of magnification.

Are you beginning to feel a little excited? "I'll get an
eyepiece of real short focal length that magnifies a thousand . . . ten thousand times. Then I can see the moon
as if it was only twenty-four miles away!"

Naturally, it isn't that easy. In practice, there is seldom
any advantage to using a magnification of more than
about 30 per inch of aperture. That is, 60 would be the
limit for a 2-inch telescope and 300 the limit on a 10-inch.
It is shown in optics that owing to the wave nature of light,
a lens cannot show a point source of light like a star as a

*point* but only as a *disk*. The larger the lens, the smaller this disk will be. Thus two stars very close together might appear as one in a 3-inch telescope. To show the stars separately, or to "resolve" the pair, you would need perhaps a 10-inch lens. A 3-inch telescope might show a double star as slightly enlongated, or dumbbell-shaped. Higher magnification would be of no help. It would only show you a bigger dumbbell. The smallest angular separation that can be detected with a telescope is given by Dawes' rule: *

$$\text{Angular separation} = 4\rlap{.}''5/a$$

where a is the aperture of the telescope in inches. Suppose you are trying to see the components of a double star $0\rlap{.}''5$ apart with a 2-inch telescope. You will never be able to see them because a 2-inch lens has a limiting resolution of $4.5/2 = 2\rlap{.}''25$. To resolve such a pair you would need at least a telescope of 9 inches aperture. Using a high-power eyepiece on your 2-inch, instead of separating the stars, would distort and blur the image and actually might show less than a lower power.

Only rarely can you attain the limit of resolution even with the best of lenses. After a few nights of observing you will begin to be very much aware of what astronomers call the "seeing." On some nights the stars look clear and sharp in your telescope. On other nights they are blurred and fuzzy, and even explode occasionally. This is not the fault of your telescope but of the atmosphere. You are familiar with the effect of "twinkling" of the stars. On nights when the stars are twinkling so beautifully, you can be sure the atmosphere is churned by air currents and the seeing very

* The Rev. W. R. Dawes, nicknamed the "eagle-eyed" for the remarkable acuity of his vision.

bad. Sometimes the seeing is so bad that astronomers are unable to observe at all even though the sky is perfectly clear.

Even in the finest refractors you can generally notice a slight fringe of color around bright objects such as Venus or the moon. This color defect in the refractor is known by the ominous name of *chromatic aberration.* The glass of the lens bends different colors by different amounts, red the least and violet the most. A simple lens is incapable of bringing all colors together to form an image at the same focus. Instead of one image of the moon, it gives a jumble of moon images, from violet through all the colors of the rainbow out to red. This confusion of colors was the most serious disadvantage in the refractor, and was not completely overcome for nearly 200 years after the invention of the telescope in 1608.

Early in the eighteenth century opticians discovered that chromatic aberration could be almost entirely eliminated by making the objective of two lenses closely fitted together, of different shape and light-bending power. Credit for designing the first achromatic (color-free) objective is usually given to John Dolland. From recent research, however, it appears that this honor should go to another Englishman, C. M. Hall, who had an achromatic objective made according to his design in 1733. (Dolland apparently saw this objective in an optical shop, grasped the idea immediately, and proceeded to get into the achromatic-telescope business.) In telescopes intended for visual work, a combination of lenses is used that brings into focus the yellow-green rays, to which the eye is most sensitive. In the best modern achromats it is possible to correct for 95 per cent of the chromatic aberration. By making the objective of three lenses, the correction can be raised to 99 per cent.


## THE MIRROR TELESCOPE, OR REFLECTOR

Around the mid-seventeenth century the situation for the refractor seemed so hopeless that Isaac Newton believed attempts to improve it should be abandoned in favor of an entirely different kind of telescope. Refraction by a lens is not the only way of bending rays to a focus. Rays can also be bent to a focus by reflection from the surface of a suitably curved mirror. Moreover, and this is the important point, a mirror bends ALL rays to the SAME focus. That is, a reflecting telescope is 100 per cent achromatic (although it suffers from other aberrations, the same as the refractor).

People are always baffled the first time they see a reflector. It doesn't look in the least the way they think a telescope should. Unlike a spyglass, it has no lens and you look in the wrong end of it. This is because the mirror which gathers light to a focus to form the image is usually out of sight at the bottom of the tube. The mirror has somewhat the shape of a saucer, although the depression in the center is so slight you might think it was flat at first glance. Light rays reflected from the surface of the mirror form an image near the upper end of the tube at the prime focus. To observe this image, an astronomer would be forced to get his head and shoulders inside the tube, which, of course, would cut off the light from the object he is trying to see. This difficulty is avoided by inserting a small flat mirror or prism inside the focus, which sends the beam to an eyepiece fixed in the side of the tube. The 200-inch telescope is so large that there is a cage at the prime focus in which the astronomer does his work, instead of carrying on observations at the side. The cage cuts off only 13 per cent of the rays from the main mirror, and is more convenient and economical of light than a mirror would be. This arrangement of the reflector is called the "Newtonian form" after Newton's original model. (Fig. 16) Auxiliary mirrors can be easily swung into place to give longer focal lengths when desired.

## RELATIVE ADVANTAGES OF REFRACTOR AND REFLECTOR

The largest lens type of telescope is the 40-inch refractor of the Yerkes Observatory of the University of Chicago, built in 1897. Opticians realized this was about the limit in size of the refractor and no lenses of larger aperture have been attempted. The larger a lens, the thicker it must be, with the result that eventually a lens becomes so thick that it absorbs more light than it gains by the increase in aperture. Since a lens must be supported around its outer edge, if too thick and heavy it is likely to bend under its own weight and give a distorted image. Also, it is difficult to cast a large piece of glass that is free from imperfections. (Fig. 17)

In the reflector, the light does not go through the glass but is reflected from a bright coating of aluminum on the surface. There is no need for the glass to be free from imperfections; in fact, the glass mirrors of great reflectors are usually full of bubbles. It is much easier to grind or "figure" a mirror to the proper shape than a lens of the same

F I G U R E   16.   Showing how the Newtonian type of reflecting telescope operates. Light from a star enters the upper open end of the tube and strikes the surface of the mirror at the bottom (not shown). The curved surface of the mirror reflects the light from the star to a small diagonal mirror near the top of the tube, which reflects it into the eyepiece at the side.

FIGURE 17.   The objective in a refracting telescope of 6 inches aperture.

size. There are hundreds, maybe thousands, of people who have built their own reflecting telescopes, but very few amateurs ever acquire the skill necessary to turn out a good objective achromat. This is the reason reflecting telescopes are so much cheaper than refractors. (Fig. 18)

There are a few things, however, to be said in behalf of the refractor. The figure of a mirror is affected by the temperature of its surroundings, so that a sudden change in the weather often results in bad images. Usually there is more scattered light in a reflector than a refractor. It is often claimed that a refractor gives better-defined images than a reflector. This the mirror makers emphatically deny today and maintain their telescopes inch for inch are the equal or superior of any lens. A mirror needs a new aluminum coat every few years to keep its reflectivity up to standard. Aluminizing has to be done at some plant where the special equipment for this job is available. An amateur cannot do it himself, as the aluminum metal has to be deposited on the surface of the mirror in a high vacuum. A refractor seldom requires attention except for cleaning the exposed surface of the objective occasionally. If moisture gets into the cell between the lens elements, however, then you are in trouble. The objective has to be taken apart carefully, and the lenses cleaned and reassembled just as carefully, or the results can be disastrous.

### THE TELESCOPE FOR COMET HUNTING

For hunting comets, a small refractor with a large ratio of aperture to focal length is desirable. Such a telescope when used with a low-power positive eyepiece gives a wide,

FIGURE 18. Framework of the 200-inch Hale reflecting telescope viewed against the sky.

bright field of view, making it easy to spot a faint diffuse object such as a comet. The telescope should be easy to manipulate and rest on a firm, secure mounting. (A woman once called to inquire if the back of a chair would be suitable for this purpose.) Sweeping for comets should be done deliberately when the observer is in a calm and serene state of mind. Such a condition is impossible to achieve if your telescope is in danger of collapse at any moment.

Strange to relate, some of the greatest comet hunters have worked with telescopes that were a far departure from this ideal type. Two of the most successful in astronomical history are Charles Messier (1730–1817) and Jean Louis Pons (1761–1831). Neither had more than an elementary knowledge of astronomy (Pons started his career as doorkeeper at the Observatory of Marseilles), and their observations were made with telescopes scarcely larger than a spyglass. Yet Messier is credited with the discovery of eighteen comets and Pons set a record with a catch of thirty-seven. They made up in perseverance what they lacked in equipment.

CHAPTER 6

# *What to do with a comet after you've discovered it*

By this time you are thoroughly aware that a comet does not look like a star with a tail attached to it, but is more likely to appear in your telescope as a faint patch of light without so much as a trace of a caudal appendage. And so you start out some night, looking hopefully for faint patches of light, hardly daring to believe that you could have the good luck to uncover a comet. To your astonishment, you run across several such faint luminous patches. Comet hunting seems almost too easy! (Fig. 19)

How often in looking through books on astronomy have you noticed star clusters and nebulae designated by the letter M, followed by some number? Well-known examples are M 31, the great galaxy in Andromeda; M 13, the star cluster in Hercules, etc. This M is the initial of Charles Messier, previously mentioned, who was plagued by the same trouble that besets all comet hunters. He kept find-

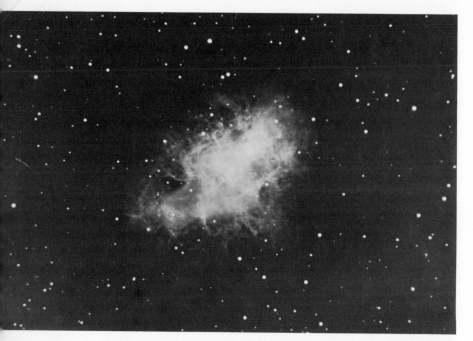

FIGURE 19.    M 1, the Crab nebula in Taurus. Charles Messier, a French comet hunter of the eighteenth century, often kept finding "comets" that later turned out to be star clusters and nebulae. For his own convenience Messier made out a catalogue of about 100 such objects, designated by his initial, of which the Crab nebula was the first.

ing "comets" that were not comets at all but only star clusters and nebulae. His hopes were dashed so often that for his own convenience he kept a list of these deceiving objects, which he published in a catalogue in 1787. There is no reason to believe that Messier had the slightest interest in these objects. They were merely a nuisance that got in the way of his comet hunting. Most of the comets Messier discovered and of which he was so proud are gone and forgotten now. But his catalogue, the by-product of his main work, turned out to be amazingly useful to astronomers. His catalogue numbers have been retained and are the principal reason Messier is still remembered today.

You have picked up a suspicious object that could be a faraway comet. You have checked carefully to make sure you have not discovered the great spiral galaxy in Triangulum or the Owl nebula in Ursa Major. No, the sky is clear in this region. Still you hesitate to proclaim your discovery to the world. You have your reputation to think of. What a blow it would be if you had slipped up somewhere. If you are in doubt, there is a test you can apply which should settle the matter beyond question.

Owing to the rotation of the earth, the stars all appear to move across the sky at a uniform rate from east to west. The comet also shares this motion of the stars. But in addition it has a motion of its own. The comet is in the solar system, moving in its orbit only a few million miles away. The stars, on the other hand, are many trillions of miles away, so distant that their motions can only be detected by measures made at intervals of several years. Thus the stars form a background of fixed reference points which we can use in following the motion of the comet. A comet usually is moving fast enough so that with a telescope its change in position can be noticed after only an hour or two. So, in case of doubt, here is what you do:

Sketch the stars easily visible in the field of view around the object, taking care to include those that are closest. When you have recorded the stars to your satisfaction, locate your suspected comet among them, and note down the time. Indicate the directions of east and north. Remember that the stars are always moving from east to west in the sky. So notice which direction the stars are drifting in the field of view and mark it *west*. The field of view as seen with an inverting eyepiece is shown in Figure 20. With a little experience you will have no difficulty determining directions in the sky. *Be sure to write everything down.* You can't trust your memory.

Besides showing the positions of the stars around your object, you should also estimate their apparent brightness or magnitude. Astronomers have adopted a scale on which a difference of one magnitude corresponds to a ratio of about 2.5 (2.512 exactly) times in brightness. This particular figure is used because it makes a bright star of magnitude 1 just 100 times as bright as a star of magnitude 6, which is about the faintest star you can see with your eye alone. To give you an idea of the magnitude scale, the seven stars that form the outline of the Big Dipper are all of the second magnitude. Sirius, the Dog Star, the brightest-appearing star in the sky except for the sun, is of magnitude $-1.5$. Vega is about magnitude 0. The apparent magnitude of the sun is $-26.5$. The faintest stars re-

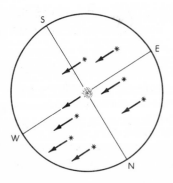

FIGURE 20. Suspected comet (center) and star field as seen with an inverting eyepiece. Directions in the sky are determined by drift of stars toward the west, as shown by arrows.

corded on photographs taken with the 200-inch reflector on Palomar Mountain are around magnitude 23. The brightness of the sun compared with these faint stars is so big as to be beyond our comprehension; but if you are interested, the sun appears to be 83 quintillion (83,180,000,000,000,-000,000) times as bright as the faintest star we are able to observe. You will have to use a star chart to become familiar with the magnitudes of telescopic stars. A star that looks bright in your telescope may be barely visible to your unaided eye.

After recording all this information, there is nothing more you can do but wait awhile to see what develops. One thing you can do while waiting is to get a fix on your object in right ascension and declination. Although these will only be rough estimates, it is information you must have if anybody else is to find your comet.

The best way to get the RA and DEC of the object is by locating its position on a star map. The RA of the stars is shown by the Roman numerals at the top and bottom of the map. The DEC is given by the numbers on the sides of the chart. If your object happens to be situated near a bright star, locating it on the map is easy. Otherwise you will have to connect it with the brighter telescopic stars nearby as best you can. Detailed instructions for doing this are given in the Appendix, together with several examples.

After a couple of hours, let us say, you check on the object again. If you are unable to detect any definite motion, or if you feel uncertain about it, you had better sleep on it for the night. If the object is still stuck in the same place among the stars the next night, you can be sure it is some star cluster or nebula that is not marked on your charts. But if the object shows unmistakable evidence of motion, the time for action has come.

What to do?

Don't telephone your old astronomy professor about it. He will not appreciate being awakened in the middle of the night, and wouldn't be of much help anyhow.

Don't waste your money on a long-distance call to some big observatory. You may not be as lucky as Nagata. If you happen to call when an astronomer is in the middle of an exposure, he may not even answer the phone. (For some reason, the telephone in the dome of a large observatory is always situated at a considerable distance from the telescope, usually at the bottom of a long flight of stairs.) In any case, you can be sure he is not going to be enraptured over the discovery of some miserable little comet. He has his observing program all planned out for the night and he is not going to interrupt it on your account.

Don't call some other amateur and tell him about it. If the object turns out to be a genuine comet he will probably claim a half interest in it later on.

What you *should* do is to inform the Central Telegram Bureau, Smithsonian Observatory, Cambridge, Mass. 02138, which serves as the clearinghouse for astronomical discoveries of all kinds. Don't notify them by an airmail letter or telephone call. Send a straight wire. A telegram constitutes a permanent record of your observation and also establishes the time of your discovery, which may be of vital importance when it comes to deciding on a name.

The telegram should include:

1. Your name.
2. The date of the observation.
3. Nature of the object discovered.

4. The universal time (UT) of the observation.

5. The RA and DEC of the object.

6. The direction of motion.

7. The magnitude.

8. A few words of description concerning the object's appearance.

From the length of this list, it looks as if you would owe most of your money to Western Union if you discovered very many comets. But it can all be condensed into about a dozen words, as follows:

PERKINS 1967 JULY 23 COMET 0630 NORTH 30    1920 NORTHWEST MAGNITUDE NINE    DIFFUSE NO TAIL.

Translated, this becomes:

PERKINS: Your last name; your full name and address will be on the telegram in any case.

1967 JULY 23: The date, referred to the meridian of Greenwich, England, or UT.

COMET: Presumable nature of the object.

0630: The UT of the observation, in this case $06^h 30^m$. If you lived in London, where the borough of Greenwich is located, this would be the time your watch would show— 6:30 on the morning of July 23. But if Perkins resides on the Pacific Coast of the United States, the time of the observation is 10:30 on the evening of July 22. (But watch out for Daylight Saving Time!) Directions for converting to UT are given in the Appendix.

NORTH 30: The declination of the object is 30° North, or $+ 30°$.

1920: The right ascension is $19^h 20^m$.

(If you care to look up this position on a star map you will find that this imaginary object is near the third-magnitude star Beta Cygni.)

NORTHWEST: An estimate of the direction of motion at the time of observation. The object is moving NORTH in the sky if its declination is INCREASING. That is, if its declination is 30°N tonight and 32°N tomorrow night, it is headed north. But if its declination were 27°N tomorrow night, its motion would be SOUTH.

If the right ascension of the object is INCREASING, it is moving EAST, as from 19$^h$ 20$^m$ tonight to 19$^h$ 37$^m$ tomorrow night. But if its right ascension tomorrow night were 19$^h$ 03$^m$ its motion is WEST.

MAGNITUDE NINE: The comet is magnitude 9, or about three magnitudes fainter than the faintest star visible to the unaided eye. A ninth-magnitude star is easily visible in only a 2-inch telescope. Since a comet is a diffuse object and not a *point* of light like a star, the magnitude estimated for a comet is naturally very uncertain.

DIFFUSE NO TAIL: Brief as it is, this description is nevertheless very helpful to others in searching for your object.

Telegrams containing this information will be sent to observatories that subscribe to this service, and an Announcement Card with more detailed information will follow by airmail later. Within a week or two, enough accurate positions of the object should be available to enable computers to calculate a preliminary orbit. Along with the orbit there will be an ephemeris, or list of approximate positions of the object for the next couple of weeks, that should be good enough to keep it from being lost. As more observations come in, they are used to correct this preliminary orbit, so that in the course of a few months a fairly reliable orbit is available. This orbit should be good enough to determine whether Comet Perkins is a periodic comet that may be seen again in another ten or twenty years, depending upon its period of revolution around the sun. But if its orbit is not a closed one and is instead essentially parabolic it will never be seen again.

The reader should not get the idea that the appearance of a new comet means that astronomers everywhere immediately drop whatever they are doing to observe it. Most of them will never do anything about it at all. They have a program of observations on which they are working, and unless their special interest happens to be in comets, they will naturally go right ahead with it. Some half a dozen comets are discovered every year on the average, mostly faint objects of minor interest. If the comet has an unusual orbit or exhibits some exceptional physical properties, it will naturally receive more attention. The public regards the discovery of a comet as an astronomical event of major importance. Very few professional astronomers deliberately look for comets, although they occasionally discover one by accident on a photograph taken for another purpose.

## WHERE IS THE BEST PLACE IN THE SKY TO LOOK FOR A COMET?

Edward Emerson Barnard (1857–1923) was an astronomer who had the unique experience of paying off the mortgage on his first home with money derived from discovering comets. Until about the age of thirty, although always interested in astronomy, circumstances compelled him to make his living in a photographic studio. He married in 1881, when times were hard and money scarcer than usual. A few months after his marriage he discovered a comet in the constellation of Pegasus, but never received credit for the discovery, as he had no knowledge of how to announce the fact. He then began searching systematically for comets and before the end of the year discovered Comet 1881 VI, which was announced to the world through the proper channels. The discovery was especially gratifying inasmuch as he received $200 from H. H. Warner, a manufacturer in Rochester, New York, who was offering such a prize to anyone discovering an unexpected comet. Barnard had spent all his ready cash on a 5-inch refractor, but the prize money enabled him to go ahead and build a small house, with the hope that the mortgage would be paid off with some more comet money. After working all day at the studio, he then sat up most of the night searching for comets. As he tells it himself:

"We could look forward only with dread to the meeting of the notes that must come due. However, the hand of Providence seemed to hover over our heads; for when the first note came due a faint comet was discovered wandering along the outskirts of creation. . . . And thus it finally came about that this house was built entirely out of comets. . . . True, it took several good-sized comets to do it; but it was done nevertheless."

Later, as a professional astronomer, Barnard discovered other comets; but his most famous discovery was not a comet, but the fifth satellite of Jupiter, an elusive little body that revolves only 69,000 miles from the planet's surface. Barnard found J V in 1892 with the 36-inch refractor at the Lick Observatory, after searching one night a week for two months. It was the last satellite to be discovered visually; all others since then have been found by photography.

When searching for comets, Barnard concentrated particularly on the western sky after sunset, and the eastern sky before sunrise. A little thought will show why these regions are likely to be rather hopeful. A comet near enough to be visible in a small telescope is either approaching the sun from outer space or has passed near the sun and is heading into deep space again. In either case it will probably be somewhere in the vicinity of the sun. Searching for an object near the sun is always difficult, as it will be hard to discern against the illumination of the twilight sky. A bright starlike object like the planet Mercury is often difficult to pick up along the dawn horizon. How much more difficult is it to spot a faint hazy object such as a comet! On one occasion it required a total eclipse of the sun to reveal a comet. As the moon cut off the last direct rays from the solar disk, a totally unexpected comet flashed out that nobody had known anything about!

Instead of looking for comets in the *same* general direction as the sun, conditions for discovery are much more favorable in the direction *opposite* the sun. This is what an astronomer means when he says he is working "in opposition." He doesn't mean that anybody is opposing him, but merely that he is observing in the opposite direction from the sun at that time. It is easy to see the advantage of working in opposition. At sunset you are scanning the sky toward the east; at midnight you are looking overhead; at dawn your telescope is pointed west. You are always observing in the darkest part of the night sky. If a comet is approaching from the opposite direction from the sun, you have a pretty good chance of finding it.

But don't forget that comets may show up anywhere. No part of the sky is safe from them. However, you would be wise to shun certain areas, such as the bowl of the Big Dipper, Cassiopeia, and Coma Berenices, which are so rich in nebulae and clusters that you will spend most of your time checking cometlike objects instead of discovering comets.

# CHAPTER 7

*The motion of comets*

Except for Mercury and Pluto, all the major planets revolve around the sun in orbits so nearly circular that the eye cannot detect the difference in a diagram. (Fig. 3) Even in the case of Mercury and Pluto, most people would probably describe their orbits as "flattened" or "kind of squashed down" circles. Until about 400 years ago everybody—or practically everybody—believed the orbits of the planets must be circles—which is almost the same thing as if they actually were circles. The thought of a planet moving in a path that was not a "perfect" circle was abhorrent, a feeling that still lingers with us today. For centuries astronomers tried to force the moon, sun, and planets all to revolve around the earth in circles, or various combinations of circles, which they obstinately refused to do. Yet some of the tables predicting the motions of the planets kept in tolerable agreement with observation for a short time. It is often remarkable how far you can go with something that is completely wrong.

In 1543 the Polish astronomer Nicolaus Copernicus published a book * in which he demonstrated that the theory of planetary motion could be considerably simplified by transferring the center of motion from the earth to the sun. A few of the ancients had believed in a heliocentric theory of motion around the sun instead of around the earth. But their theories were of a mystical nature that had little basis in observation. As early as 500 B.C. Philolaus had advocated the revolution of the earth around a central fire. By the sixteenth century, however, these old heliocentric theories had been forgotten or discarded as unworthy of serious consideration. The Copernican theory still retained the idea of strictly circular motion. It was not so radical as generally believed.

The next great advance was discovery of the three laws of planetary motion by the German astronomer, astrologer, mathematician, meteorologist, and writer of popular scientific books, Johannes Kepler (1571–1630). Kepler derived these laws from a long series of observations of Mars made by his former employer, the famous Danish astronomer Tycho Brahe. Tycho's observations were by far the most accurate made before the invention of the telescope. Kepler tried one combination of circular motions after another in a vain attempt to find a system that would be in accurate agreement with observation. After an appalling amount of this cut-and-try sort of labor, he finally obtained two laws, which he published in 1609. His third or "har-

---

* *De revolutionibus orbium coelestium.* An advance copy reached Copernicus on May 24, 1543, the day of his death.

monic" law was not announced until ten years later. The wonder is that he was able to accomplish anything at all. His salary was always in arrears; his wife became sick with fever, epilepsy, and fits, of which she died; his three children died of smallpox; and Prague, where he was living, became a battlefield. The life of an Imperial Mathematician was not a simple one.

Kepler discovered that the planets do *not* move around the sun in circles or some combination of circles, but revolve in a type of closed curve, closely akin to a circle, called the *ellipse*. In fact, the circle is really a special kind of ellipse. You can try drawing an ellipse if you like by setting two thumbtacks in a drawing board, passing a loop of string around them, and then, keeping the string taut, drawing a curve around the tacks with a pencil. (I have never been able to draw a successful ellipse in this way, but the reader may be more skillful.) Putting the two thumbtacks farther apart produces a more elongated ellipse. If they are very far apart, the ellipse roughly resembles the shape of a cigar or cucumber. Conversely, the closer the tacks are placed to each other, the more nearly the resulting curve resembles a circle. In fact, if the two tacks could be superposed, the curve that results *is* a circle.

We can see now how astonishing it would be if a body moved in a path such that it was *always* at *exactly* the *same* distance from the sun at *every* point in its orbit. Even if a body were started revolving in a circular orbit, the slightest disturbance would change it to an ellipse. Motion around the sun in a circle is such a very special kind of an orbit that we can never hope to achieve it in reality.

It will save time later if we learn a few technical terms relating to the ellipse. (Remember, we're in the space age

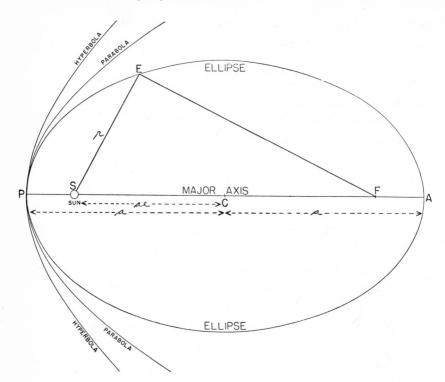

FIGURE 21. The shape of an ellipse is determined by the ratio of the distance between its foci, SF, to the length of its major axis, PA.

now and you have to know about some of these things if you don't want to become a back number.)

The two thumbtacks are the *foci* of the ellipse. The line drawn through the foci from one end of the ellipse to the other is the *major axis*. Half its length is the *semi-major axis,* or the *mean distance.* We have seen that the greater the separation of the thumbtacks (foci), the more elongated is the resulting ellipse. But the information that the foci of an ellipse are 3 inches apart or 50 million miles apart doesn't give another person a clear picture of its shape.

This information is provided by the *eccentricity* of the ellipse, denoted by *e*. Suppose that in Figure 21, the distance between the foci, SF, is 10 inches, and the length of the major axis, PA, is 13 inches. The ratio of SF to PA is then SF/PA = 10/13 = 0.77. An ellipse drawn to these specifications is slightly oblate, shaped somewhat like a cantaloupe. In Figure 22 we see an ellipse vastly different in size, for which the separation between the foci is 69 million miles and the length of the major axis is 73 million miles. These figures are in the ratio 69/73 = 0.945, and give us a long slender ellipse with a shape that reminds us of a cigar. To find the shape of an ellipse, it is evident that we do not need to go to the effort of drawing it to scale; all we need to know is the ratio SF/PA, or its eccentricity.

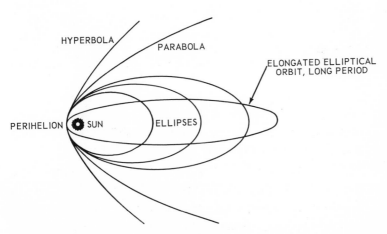

FIGURE 22. Four ellipses of different eccentricity, and two other related curves, the parabola and hyperbola.

Now you will probably have a pretty good idea of the shape of the orbits of the various objects listed in Table 3, merely by noting their eccentricities in the last column.

We see that the major planets and the moon have orbits of small or moderate eccentricity which depart only slightly in shape from circles. Ceres, the largest asteroid, has an orbit of low eccentricity, as do most of the other bodies in the asteroid belt. Encke's comet and Halley's comet revolve in orbits of high eccentricity, approaching

## T A B L E  3

## Orbital Eccentricities of Various Types of Objects in the Solar System

| Name | Type of object | Eccentricity $(e)$ of orbit |
|------|----------------|------------------------------|
| Mercury | Major planet | 0.2066 |
| Venus | Major planet | .0068 |
| Earth | Major planet | .0168 |
| Neptune | Major planet | .0090 |
| Pluto | Major planet | .2486 |
| Moon | Satellite | .0549 |
| Ceres | Asteroid | .077 |
| Hidalgo | Asteroid | .65 |
| Icarus | Asteroid | .79 |
| P/Encke | Periodic comet | .85 |
| P/Halley | Periodic comet | .97 |
| P/1925II | Periodic comet | 0.142 |

1.0, as do most of the comets. But notice that not ALL asteroids move in approximately circular orbits, for Hidalgo and Icarus have orbits of cometary eccentricity. And neither do ALL comets move in highly eccentric orbits, for P/1925II has an eccentricity less than that of Mercury and Pluto. Even a table as brief as this one raises some interesting questions.

The sun is always located at one of the foci of a planet's orbit. The other focus is vacant and of no special interest to us. The point on the orbit nearest the sun is called *perihelion*. The point on the orbit farthest from the sun is *aphelion*. In the case of the moon's orbit around the earth, the corresponding names are *perigee* and *apogee*, respectively. These statements are contained in Kepler's first law of planetary motion: "The orbit of every planet is an ellipse with the sun at one of its foci." It tells us the type of curve in which the planets revolve around the sun, and where the sun is situated within it.

How does a planet move in its orbit? The answer is given by Kepler's second law of planetary motion: "The line joining the planet with the sun sweeps over equal areas in equal intervals of time."

This law is easiest understood by reference to a diagram (Figure 23). The shaded regions in the orbit, B, C, and D, show three areas swept over by the line joining the planet and sun in ten days each. Although they differ widely in shape, it can be proved that all have the same area. When the planet is near the perihelion of its orbit at P, the line from planet to sun is *shortest*. But it is at perihelion that the planet is moving the *fastest*. At aphelion, A, the line from planet to sun is longest but its motion is the slowest. The two effects combine so that the areas cov-

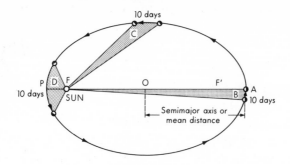

FIGURE 23.    Illustrating Kepler's law of areas. The line joining the planet and sun sweeps over the same area of its orbit in the same time.

ered in ten days are equal. The same is true for the area covered in any ten-day interval at some intermediate position, C.

The third law tells us the relation between the size of a planet's orbit and its period of revolution. Kepler called this the "harmonic" law, as he related it in some obscure way to the harmonies of the world or musical scale of the heavens. Saturn and Jupiter formed the bass of the celestial choir, Mars the tenor, Earth and Venus the alto, and Mercury the soprano. (Kepler's scientific reputation would be much higher today if a lot of his writing had gone into the flames of some big book-burning spectacular back in the seventeenth century.) According to the third law, "The squares of the periods in which the planets revolve around the sun are proportional to the cubes of their mean distances from the sun."

Let us see how well his third law holds for Mars. Mars revolves around the sun in a period of 687 days, or 1.88

years. Its mean distance, or semi-major axis, is 1.52 AU. Now we have:

$$(\text{Period})^2 = 1.88 \times 1.88 = 3.534$$
$$(\text{Mean distance})^3 = 1.52 \times 1.52 \times 1.52 = 3.511.$$

The two are nearly equal—as they should be. The same relationship will be found to hold true for the other planets if you care to go through the arithmetic. Kepler's joy knew no bounds at this discovery. It was one of the few bright spots in a life filled with suffering and disappointments.

Although Kepler discovered these laws, he never knew WHY the planets obeyed them. Why do the planets move in ellipses? There are many other types of closed curves. Why don't they revolve around the sun in the heart-shaped figure called the cardioid? Why should the *square* of the period be equal to the *cube* of the mean distance? Why not the 13/4 power of the distance? Kepler speculated at considerable length on these matters but arrived at nothing of significance.

It took the genius of Isaac Newton a half century later to prove that Kepler's three laws were not three separate and distinct statements of the way a planet moves. Newton showed that all three laws are simply different consequences of the single law of universal gravitation. We will state this law here to have it on record, although in a book such as this we cannot discuss it in any detail.

"Every particle of matter in the universe attracts every other particle with a force that is directly proportional to the product of their masses, and inversely proportional to the square of the distance between them."

To the nonmathematical reader this law may not sound

so simple. But think how much simpler it is than most of our man-made laws!

We can hardly say that Newton "discovered" gravity. For quite a few thousand years before Newton appeared on the scene, people had known that leaves fall, water runs downhill, and that boulders are heavy. When we see something all the time, after a while we are liable not to notice it at all. Newton, in a sudden flash of insight, realized that the same force which caused an apple to fall from a tree in his garden might also be the force that keeps the moon revolving in its orbit.

We speak of bodies as always falling "down." But which way is "down"? "Down" at the south pole is in the opposite direction from "down" at the north pole. What we really mean is that all bodies fall toward the center of the earth.* It can be demonstrated mathematically that the earth attracts bodies at its surface and beyond as if its whole mass were concentrated at its center (a proposition that Newton had great difficulty in proving).

Many careful measurements have shown that at the surface of the earth bodies always fall at the same rate: 16 feet the first second, 48 feet the next, 80 feet the third second, and so on.** (In everything that follows in this chapter, atmospheric resistance is neglected.) Whether a body weighs 1 pound or 100 pounds, consists of solid gold or plastic, and is hot or cold, makes no difference: all

---

* The direction of gravity is influenced slightly by the presence of a large mass such as a mountain.

** These are rough, approximate values. The acceleration of gravity is greatest at the poles and decreases toward the equator. The standard value adopted is 32.174 feet/sec².

bodies at the surface of the earth fall at the same rate in a vacuum. Also, its motion under gravity is independent of any other motion given to it. Let a body fall vertically from rest from a cliff 1000 feet high. It will strike the ground after 7.9 seconds. Throw it horizontally as far as you can. Again it will strike the ground after 7.9 seconds.

If you tried this experiment from very great elevations above the surface, however, the results would differ. According to the law of gravitation, the force of gravity varies inversely, or *decreases,* as the distance from the center of attraction *increases.* Imagine yourself 4000 miles above the earth. Now you are 8000 miles from the center, which is twice as far as when you are at the surface. So the force of gravity is not one-*half* as much, but one-*fourth* as much (since the force of attraction changes inversely as the *square* of the distance). Now the body would fall more slowly, 4 . . . 12 . . . 20 . . . feet in successive seconds. (But its velocity would not increase at a steady rate as it does at the surface, since it is approaching the earth and the attraction of gravity increasing.)

It has always been customary to illustrate the motion of a satellite around the earth by firing a cannon ball from the summit of an impossibly high peak. (You have to hurry to get the cannon out of the way before the ball comes around again.) We are going to update this experiment by launching satellites at our command from an elevation of 500 miles above the surface, or 4500 miles from the center of the earth. Our satellites will be launched with different speeds but always perpendicular to the direction of the center of the earth. What we want to do is to put an artificial satellite into an orbit that has the same shape, or eccentricity, as the moon. The orbit of the moon has an eccentricity of $e = 0.055$, so small that its shape is hard to distinguish from a circle.

The man in charge of this project isn't much for figures but prefers to get results by trying something and seeing what happens. He launches the first satellite with a velocity of 3.10 miles per second. (Fig. 24a) The satellite goes into orbit all right but doesn't get very far. The trouble is that the satellite falls toward the earth faster than the surface of the earth curves away from it, with the result that it crashes after 26 minutes, going only about a quarter of the way around the globe. The satellite was trying to revolve in an ellipse which has the center of the earth for one of its foci. But, as the diagram shows, most of the orbit lies within the solid body of the earth itself, and so is of theoretical interest only.

Clearly, the satellite needs more velocity. So on the next shot it is sent into orbit at 4.47 miles per second. This time it goes considerably farther. Unfortunately, it doesn't quite clear the surface on the opposite side of the earth, so that the experiment ends again in disaster. (Fig. 24b)

The engineer approaches the third shot with grim determination, resolved the satellite shall make it all the way around this time. So he starts it with a launch velocity of 5.26 miles per second. Now he finds he has overshot the mark. The satellite recedes to 8357 miles at apogee, soaring 4357 miles above the surface in an orbit nearly six times more eccentric than the moon's. (Fig. 24c)

Now he is desperate. With his job at stake, this fourth try must be a success. He gives the satellite a launch velocity of 4.736 miles per second, and that does it. The satellite revolves around the earth in a period of 111 minutes 12 seconds in an orbit shaped just like the moon's.

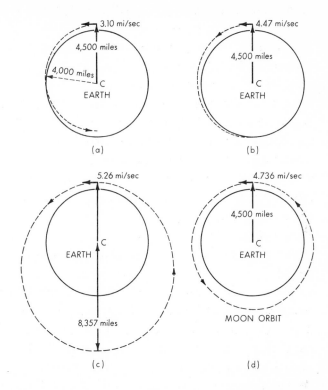

FIGURE 24. (a). Path of an artificial satellite launched from an elevation of 500 miles above the surface with a velocity of 3.10 miles per second. The satellite crashes about a quarter of the way around earth. Dotted line shows path satellite would follow if earth were not in the way. (b). Satellite launched with velocity of 4.47 miles per second goes about half-way around earth but does not quite clear the surface. (c). A velocity of 5.26 miles per second sends the satellite soaring in a much larger orbit than desired. (d). A satellite launched from height of 500 miles with velocity of 4.736 miles per second would have orbit of same shape as our moon.

We could make the moon revolve in its present orbit by proceeding in essentially the same way, although not by this cut-and-try process we have used for illustration purposes. The orbit of the moon happens to be almost exactly 60 radii of the earth away, which is 60 × 4000 = 240,000 miles. Therefore, the force of attraction is $60^2 = 3600$ times less than at the earth's surface. This makes it easier for us, as we need not give the moon nearly so much initial velocity as the satellite. Calculation shows that a velocity at launch of about 0.64 miles per second in a direction perpendicular to the earth would be all we need.

Newton developed the theory of the motion of celestial bodies under gravitation in 1665 when he was twenty-three years old. He tried to check his theory by calculating the rate at which the moon "falls" toward the earth as it revolves in its orbit. Although theory and observation agreed fairly well, he nevertheless delayed announcing the law of gravitation until twenty years later. (Anybody who made such a discovery today would rush into print immediately.) The explanation usually offered for the delay is that the radius of the earth was not accurately known, and Newton decided to wait until a better value became available. But from modern research into Newton's papers it seems very doubtful if this could have been the reason. Why Newton was so excessively cautious on this matter is one of several things we don't understand about this strange genius.

You may have been wondering, what if a comet comes along that doesn't know it is supposed to move in an elliptical orbit with an eccentricity of less than 1? Suppose it got itself into an orbit with an eccentricity equal to 1, or even more than 1. What then?

As the empty focus moves farther and farther from the focus occupied by the sun, the orbit becomes more elongated, and its eccentricity becomes 0.999 . . . 0.9999 . . . 0.99999 . . . . nearly 1.00000! But not until the empty focus were removed to "infinity" would it finally attain an eccentricity of 1. "Infinity" is a mathematical fiction, not so easily defined as is ordinarily supposed. For our present purposes, conceive of the greatest distance imaginable. Well, regardless of how great it may be, infinity is still greater.

When the empty focus is removed to infinity the eccentricity becomes 1, and we no longer have an ellipse, but another curve called a *parabola*. The parabola is not a closed curve like the ellipse, but consists of two branches which become parallel to each other at infinity. During the short time we can observe a comet while near the sun, it is often impossible to determine whether it is moving in a parabola or an extremely elongated ellipse. It is common practice to assume that *any* newly discovered comet is moving in a parabola, until its orbit can be better defined, as more observations become available. (Fig. 22)

If the eccentricity exceeds 1, the curve is called a *hyperbola*. This also consists of an open curve of two branches extending to infinity. But unlike the parabola, the two branches never become parallel but diverge from each other at some particular angle at infinity. The higher the eccentricity, the greater the angle of divergence. So far, no comet is known that was moving in a hyperbola *before* entering the solar system. Several comets have made their *exit* from the solar system via hyperbola. But when traced back, no comet has ever been found to have been moving in an orbit that was definitely hyperbolic when at a great distance from the solar system. It became hyperbolic *after* entering the solar system, owing to a close encounter with one of the giant planets, usually Jupiter.

Hyperbolic orbits demand higher velocities than bodies are likely to attain in the natural course of events. Consider some velocities in the solar system. The earth revolves around the sun at a distance of 1 AU with a nearly uniform velocity of 18.5 miles per second. Halley's comet moves in an elongated elliptical orbit of eccentricity 0.967. Its velocity at the orbit of the earth is 25.79 miles per second. To move in a parabola or hyperbola, it would need a velocity of 26.15 miles per second or more at the earth's orbit. Should it attain such a high velocity, it would escape from the solar system never to return. The escape velocity is smaller at greater distances: 8.1 miles per second at the distance of Jupiter and 2.9 miles per second at Pluto. To escape from the surface of a body of such small mass as the earth requires a velocity of not quite 7 miles per second. A body moving with this velocity would never return to the earth but would be unable to escape from the sun.

We shall have more to say about high-velocity hyperbolic orbits when we come to the origin of comets.

# CHAPTER 8

# *The six elements*
# *of the orbit*

A new comet has been discovered. We photograph it for several weeks against the background of the fixed stars. We ask ourselves, is it likely to become a spectacularly bright object? How far is it from the sun? How close will it come to the earth? Will it be well situated for observation? Is it moving in a small elliptical orbit which will bring it back in a few years? Or will we never see it again?

The photographs give us no immediate answer to these questions. All they tell us is the direction of the comet on the celestial sphere at the times of observation. They give us no direct information on its distance, velocity, or orbit. Yet from only three observations of the comet's position it is possible, in theory at least, to find out everything we want to know about its motion, past and future. The necessary mathematical processes were devised more than a century ago by Pierre Simon Laplace (1749–1827) in

France, and Carl Friedrich Gauss (1777–1855) in Germany. (Gauss, incidentally, was one of the few great mathematicians the world has known who liked numerical computation. Most professional mathematicians are no good when it comes to arithmetic. They are used to thinking in terms of symbols and seldom descend to anything as lowly as ordinary numbers.) Although their orbit methods have been worked over and refined in hundreds of papers, the principles upon which they were based remain essentially unchanged. Here we are not concerned with the technical details of orbit determination, however, but rather with the information the orbit gives us once somebody has determined it.

We cannot specify the position of anything, whether it be a comet in the solar system or a jar on the pantry shelf, without first establishing some sort of reference system for measuring distances and directions. In a city we do this, often in a way calculated to drive the inhabitants to distraction, by means of streets and house numbers. Usually there are two main thoroughfares, one running north-south and the other east-west, with the other streets forming a network parallel to them. This enables Mr. Brown to tell people that his office is in the building on the southwest corner of West 100th Street and North 50th Avenue. (Fig. 25) If necessary, he can specify its location in three-dimensional space: his office is on the tenth floor by the back stairs. The methods used in fixing positions in the solar system may seem confusing to you at first because they are new to you. Actually, they are much simpler than the numbers attached to the jumble of streets, avenues, boulevards, drives, and alleys that confound the stranger in our cities.

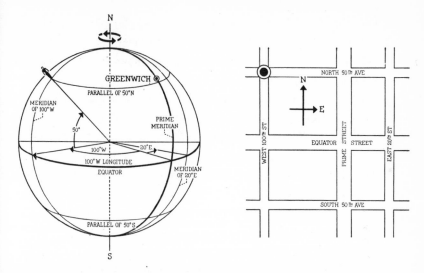

FIGURE 25.   How points are located on the surface of the earth. The meridians of longitude correspond to streets running north and south. The parallels of latitude to streets running east and west The man is located at the point where the meridian of 100° W. longitude crosses the parallel of 50° N. latitude. (From *A Brief Text in Astronomy* by Skilling and Richardson, Holt-Dryden, rev. ed., 1959.)

In the solar system it is convenient to refer the motion of a body to the orbit of the earth as the basic plane of reference. This plane is not, of course, limited to merely the 1 AU of distance that the earth's orbit describes around the sun. Instead we think of this plane as extending indefinitely into space until it cuts the surface of the celestial sphere. As the earth revolves in its orbit, it seems to us as if we were standing still and the sun was doing all the moving, pursuing (practically) the same path year after year against the background of the stars. The fact that we cannot see stars near the sun is of no matter. We know their positions and can readily determine the position of the sun among them at any time, whether the stars are visible or not. This apparent path that the sun describes among the stars each year is called the *ecliptic,* so named because eclipses of the sun and moon must always occur on this path. The ecliptic is not an invention of the space age but has been used by astronomers for probably 3000 years at least.

Another basic plane of reference in the sky is the plane passing through the equator of the earth. Again you must imagine this plane as extending from the center of the earth indefinitely in all directions in space. This reference plane is appropriately named the *celestial equator.*

Suppose the ecliptic and celestial equator actually had thin planes passing through them extending an infinite distance into space. If we could see them in the sky they would appear to us from our viewpoint on the earth as seen in Figure 26. You as the observer always feel as if you were at the center of the universe. Notice that the line of intersection of the ecliptic with the celestial sphere meets the line of intersection of the celestial equator at a considerable angle. This is because the equator of the earth is tilted at an angle of $23°5$ to the ecliptic. If the equator, or axis of rotation of the earth, were not tilted relative to its orbit there would be no seasons.

Imagine that the stars are visible near the sun, as they would be if it were not for the diffusion of the sun's rays by the atmosphere. Beginning, say, about March 19, you plot the position of the sun among the stars each day. Your

FIGURE 26. The observer always feels that he is at the center of the celestial sphere. Celestial equator and ecliptic are shown as they might appear if visible in sky. (From *A Brief Text in Astronomy* by Skilling and Richardson, Holt-Dryden, rev. ed., 1959.)

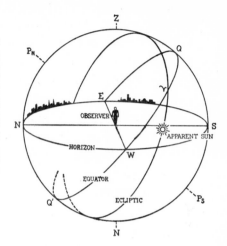

chart would show that the sun is apparently moving among the stars as indicated in Figure 27, by a distance equal to twice its width per day. The sun is approaching the celestial equator from the south side, and on March 21 crosses to the north side. The point at which the sun crosses the celestial equator from south to north marks the position of the *vernal equinox,* and the time of crossing the beginning of spring. (The date is usually March 21 but may vary by a day because of leap year.) The point on the celestial equator where the sun crosses from the north side to the south side, about September 21, marks the position of the *autumnal equinox.*

We often refer to the vernal equinox as if it were a material point out in space put there for our convenience like a traffic signal. Actually, the vernal equinox is simply a *direction* in space. It is marked on star maps by the symbol ♈, representing the horns of a ram. You might think

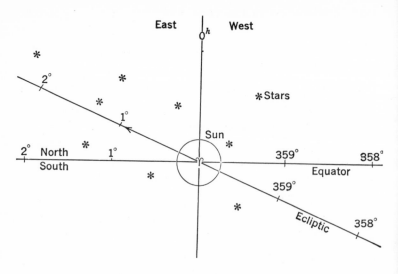

FIGURE 27.   Apparent path of sun on March 21 at vernal equinox ( ♈ ) if stars were visible in daytime.

of the vernal equinox as somewhat like a sign with an arrow reading *This way* → EAST. The arrow tells you which direction is east. But no matter how far you travel in that direction you never get to "east."

Owing to a slow conical motion of the earth's axis in space, the sun in its yearly eastward motion does not cross the celestial equator at precisely the same point each March 21, but a little to the west each time. This westward motion of the equinox is called *precession*, and was discovered about 150 B.C. by Hipparchus. The vernal equinox was then in the constellation of Aries the Ram, which explains the form of its symbol. Although in the last 2000 years the vernal equinox has, so to speak, backed into the next constellation to the west, Pisces the Fishes, the old symbol is still retained.

When speaking of the position of points on the earth, we cannot always locate them by their street number, especially if the point happens to be in the middle of the Pacific Ocean. Instead we use a reference system of a more general nature applicable anywhere. (Fig. 25) Distances north and south of the earth's equator are called *latitude*. The distance from the equator to the north pole is 90°. A place halfway between the equator and north pole would be in latitude 45°N; a point one-third of the distance from the equator to the south pole would be in latitude 30°S; and so on. Distances in an east or west direction are measured in terms of *longitude*. Lines called meridians are drawn from pole to pole perpendicular to the equator. Since all meridians look alike, we have had to select one arbitrarily and designate it as the *prime meridian*. It has been agreed that the meridian through the position formerly occupied by the Royal Observatory at Greenwich, England, shall be the zero, or prime, meridian from which longitude is counted. Distances measured west from Greenwich, or opposite to the direction of the earth's rotation, are counted from 0° to 180° of west longitude; distances measured from Greenwich in the direction of the earth's rotation are counted from 0° to 180° of east longitude. For example, the latitude of New York is 41°N, and its longitude 74°W; Los Angeles is in latitude 34°N, longitude 118°W; Paris is in longitude 49°N, longitude 2°E; Rio de Janeiro is about latitude 23°S, longitude 43°W.

Similarly, we can specify positions in the sky by their celestial latitude and longitude. Celestial latitude is the angular distance of an object measured to the north or south from the ecliptic. Celestial longitude is the angular distance measured eastward along the ecliptic from the vernal equinox. *Eastward* is always measured in the direction of the sun's yearly motion among the stars of about 1° per day, due to the revolution of the earth around the sun. It should not be confused with the apparent daily westward motion of the sun due to the rotation of the earth on its axis. Longitude on the earth is measured from 0° to 180° east or west from Greenwich. But celestial longitude is measured always toward the east from 0° at the vernal equinox, around the sky through 360°, back to the vernal equinox.

We are now ready to talk about the elements of an orbit of a comet, planet, or whatever the body may be. We will introduce them first and then tell you about them. The elements are:

*a*, The semi-major axis of the orbit, which tells us its size.

*e*, The eccentricity of the orbit, which defines its shape.

*i*, The inclination of the plane of the orbit to the ecliptic.

☊, The longitude of the orbit's ascending node. This formidable-sounding element is the angular distance measured eastward from the vernal equinox to the point where the object crosses the ecliptic from south to north. The opposite point on the orbit, where the body moves from the north to the south side of the ecliptic, is the descending node ☋. The straight line drawn through the ascending node, Sun, and descending node is the *line of nodes*.

ω, The argument of the perihelion. It is the angular distance from the ascending node in the plane of the orbit to the perihelion point, measured in the direction of the object's motion. Notice that ω is measured in the *plane of the orbit* and *not* in the plane of the ecliptic.

These five elements completely describe the *orbit* of a comet, asteroid, or planet. But they fail to tell us where the comet is at any particular moment *in its orbit*. Once we know its position at a certain time, we can start the comet moving as if it were a train running on a railroad track, and calculate its position at any time in the past or future. This sixth element that locates the comet for us in its orbit is the *epoch*, T. It is usually the time of last perihelion passage.

Figure 28 shows the elements of the asteroid Icarus, which moves in a quasi-cometary orbit. The light area indicates the plane of the ecliptic in which the earth revolves. The plane through the orbit of Icarus is indicated by the dark area. The angle between the dark and light planes is the inclination, which for Icarus is 23°. The dotted portion of the Icarus orbit shows that part which is below, or south of, the ecliptic. The continuous line shows the portion of the orbit above the ecliptic. The ascending node is at the point on the orbit where the broken line becomes continuous measured in the direction of Icarus' motion. The descending node is at the point on the orbit where the continuous line becomes a broken line. The longitude of the ascending node is measured eastward from the direction of the vernal equinox, indicated by the black broken arrow, in the ecliptic (light) plane, to the straight solid line marking the line of nodes. The argu-

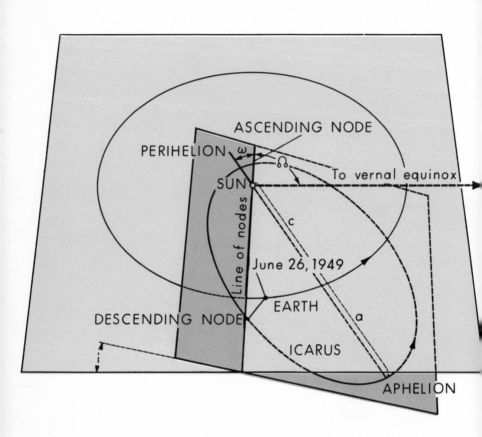

ment, ω, is meaured from the ascending node *in the direction of the object's motion and in the plane of the orbit* (dark), to the perihelion point.

For Icarus, *a* is 1.0777 AU (100.2 million miles), *i* is 22°.979, ☊ is 87°.746, and ω is 30°.912. The date of Icarus' first perihelion passage after its discovery was June 4, 1950.

FIGURE 28. Computation of asteroid orbit requires determination of six elements, which can be expressed in many ways.
Five elements are needed to describe size, shape, and orientation
of the ellipse itself; the sixth gives the asteroid's position at a
particular time. The size and shape of the ellipse are given by
two elements: the length of the semi-major axis, *a*, and the eccentricity, *e*, defined as *c/a*, where *c* is the distance from the sun
to the center of the ellipse. A third element, *i*, gives the angle
between the plane of the asteroid's orbit and that of the earth's.
A fourth element, $\Omega$, is the longitude of the ascending node.
It is the angular distance measured eastward in the plane of
the earth's orbit, or ecliptic, from the vernal equinox to the
point where the asteroid crosses the ecliptic from south to
north. A fifth element, $\omega$ (small omega), defines how the major
axis of the ellipse is oriented in its orbital plane by giving the
angle between the ascending node and the perihelion point,
measured in the plane of the asteroid's orbit and in the direction of the asteroid's motion. The sixth element is usually given
as the time when the asteroid passes perihelion. For Icarus *a*
is 1.0777 astronomical units (100.2 million miles), *e* is 0.827, *i*
is 22.979 degrees, $\Omega$ is 87.746 degrees, and $\omega$ is 30.912 degrees.
(Angles in diagram appear somewhat distorted owing to perspective of drawing.) (From "The Discovery of Icarus" by
Robert S. Richardson, *Scientific American*, April 1965.)

In June 1968, Icarus and the earth will be in nearly the
same positions relative to each other as they were at discovery in June 1949. This time Icarus will be above and
slightly behind the earth, when it will be distant only
4,200,000 miles on June 15, 1968, at closest approach. The
diameter of Icarus is about 1 mile.

# CHAPTER 9

## *Collision of a comet with the earth*

"What would happen if a comet hit the earth?"

People often ask astronomers that question but seldom get a satisfactory answer, or any answer at all. The reason is that nobody knows. It depends entirely upon the nature of the nucleus. If the nucleus consists of light, fragile material, the earth should come through in pretty good shape. But if the nucleus consists of chunks of stone and iron, the consequences could be very serious indeed.

We shall try to trace the course of events leading up to a collision of a large comet with the earth, but the actual collision will be left to your imagination.

We will suppose the comet is picked up accidentally on a plate taken by Dr. Willard Hickson of the Careworn Observatory. The comet, although only thirteenth magnitude, has a faint halo around it which enabled Hickson to detect its nonstellar character at once. During the next two weeks his plates showed the object was moving slowly eastward and north, and by setting off its motion during his 60-minute exposures he was able to bring out the coma distinctly. After Hickson's time was up on the mountain, he turned over all his plates to Dr. Arnold Pettigrew, an orbit expert, who regarded them with scant enthusiasm. After disposing of his loot, Hickson loaded his family into the old car and headed in the general direction of Mount Ixtacihuatl, Mexico, for a long-delayed vacation. Once on the road, he promptly forgot about the comet as if it had never existed.

It took Pettigrew a week to identify his comparison stars, measure his plates, and calculate the comet's coordinates. But once these chores were out of the way, he had the orbit within a few hours. Another retrograde comet. His interest in Object Hickson began to pick up slightly. This comet certainly must be a big one. Although some 300 days from perihelion passage and 4.2 A.U. from the sun, it was brighter than a lot of comets at half that distance. Old Hickson had latched onto something good for once. The next day Pettigrew sent a finding ephemeris to Cambridge, along with a request to the astronomical world for some more observations.

Hickson had discovered the object on August 1 while photographing M 80, the globular cluster in Scorpio. Fortunately, good weather prevailed for several months, so that there was no lack of observations to improve the orbit. By late October the comet was almost lost in the sunset sky and would not be well placed for observation again in the morning sky till around the first of the year.

It was while computing an ephemeris for the coming apparition that Pettigrew was first struck by the exceptionally close approach of the comet about the middle of next April. (Fig. 29) His figures made it 0.0051 AU, hardly twice the distance of the moon. About the same time several other astronomers over the world also began to awaken to this interesting circumstance. Shpighelsky at Poulkovo had a geocentric distance of 0.0023 AU, slightly closer than the moon. He could be right, too, Pettigrew mused. Shpighelsky was a good man. And what was this! Triandafyllidis at Athens got a value of .00091 AU! Why not call it a smashup and be done with it?

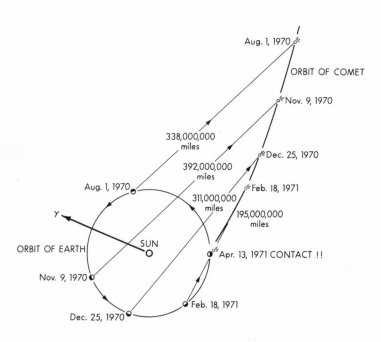

FIGURE 29.   How the earth and a comet moving in nearly parabolic orbit might collide. This encounter, although purely imaginary, has been worked out in accordance with mathematical theory of comet motion.

In a former era, an announcement about some innocent little comet might have passed unnoticed by the press. But times change. Newspapers now employ bright young men whose job is to keep an eye on science. One in particular made a point of always taking a good hard look at the I.A.U. Announcement Cards. (He had gotten scooped on a supernova once and vowed it would never happen again.) The result was that next day readers of the morning papers found themselve confronted by the disturbing news GIANT COMET TO COLLIDE WITH EARTH? By a coincidence, the item was released at a time when big news was rather slack. As a consequence, the story ballooned out of all proportion to its real importance. When Hickson returned from his vacation, physically exhausted and financially depleted, he found that he had succeeded in achieving fame without the slightest effort on his part. His telephone rang all day. He was interviewed on TV. There were photographs of Hickson looking at a photograph of Comet Hickson. He was shown peering through the finder of his telescope, presumably in search of Comet Hickson (until somebody pointed out they had forgotten to open the shutter in the dome). On Sunday there was a syndicated story illustrated by a diagram in which the earth and comet were coming closer and closer, with a big question mark where their paths intersected.

As soon as the comet came in view again in the morning sky and new observations began coming in, the orbit men went to work on it in earnest. Previously, they had computed its motion as if the other planets did not exist, and the sun and comet were the only bodies in space. Now they determined its motion including the disturbing attraction of Jupiter, Mars, and the earth-moon system.

The results were not reassuring: Comet Hickson was coming close, all right. And by the end of February there was no use evading the issue: comet and earth were on collision trajectories.

People had disregarded the collision story when it first appeared. Something terrible was always happening or about to happen. You couldn't worry about everything. But this time the situation could not be shrugged off so easily. The whole thing seemed incredible. You would forget about it for awhile. Then it would come stealing into your thoughts again at the strangest times: while you were shaving, or writing a check, or dressing for a party. It made everything you were doing seem utterly useless. You would stop in the middle of a sentence or find yourself staring blankly into your empty coffee cup.

The paralyzing thing about the situation was the rapidity with which it developed. One day the comet was just a name out there in space, millions of miles away. Then overnight it was *here*, an enormous object in the sky, bigger than a dozen full moons. Even astronomers forgot that they were scientists, staring at the ghostly intruder.

When the comet was only two weeks away, the sense of futility became overwhelming. Some people were gripped with a sort of frenzy. They had to have something to do, someone to talk to, every minute . . . every second. They became intensely preoccupied in a ceaseless round of petty activities whose only objective was the avoidance of reality. Night was the hard part—the hours alone when they had to come to terms with themselves.

A considerable number of people, however, continued going about their business pretty much as usual. It was not that they were so courageous, or had some philosophy of life that made them indifferent to their fate. It was because they were simply incapable of believing that anything could disturb the placid routine of their well-ordered lives. They had held their job for twenty years, hadn't they? It was impossible to get fired now. They had their pension fund. Their insurance was paid up. So what could happen to them?

Finally the truth began to penetrate. War, scandal, murder—everything gave way to the comet. Why didn't somebody *do* something? There must be *something*. . . .

During the last week, scientists and their high-speed computers worked ceaselessly in an effort to pinpoint the time and place of collision. According to Pettigrew, the collision would occur in the Charski Mountains of eastern Siberia. Shpighelsky declared contact would occur at longitude 120° 37′ W, latitude 39°N, which investigation revealed was the position of Reno, Nevada. The Royal Observatory hopefully had Comet Hickson diving into Hudson Bay. The wide scatter in their predictions arose from the diffuse nature of the nucleus, which made accurate observations of position impossible. Ordinarily, an uncertainty of a few thousand miles in a comet's position would have been of no consequence. But this was no ordinary occasion. And so one place on the globe was no safer than another. There was no means of defense . . . no easy escape . . . nothing to do but wait.

The degree of damage inflicted by a comet would naturally depend upon where it landed. So far as our *planet* Earth is concerned, the damage would be negligible. The astronomers on Mars would report that the earth looked just about the same. If the comet struck in the ocean or a barren region around one of the poles, we should survive it all right. Doubtless there would be earthquakes and strong seismic waves, or *tsunamis,* and peculiar meteorological effects that should keep geophysicists happily occupied for years to come. But the loss of life would be trifling. If contact occurred in a densely populated region, however, there is no minimizing the fact that the devastation could conceivably be worse than dumping the world's supply of atomic bombs on the spot. Still . . . the damage would be of a superficial nature. It is doubtful if the length of the day or year or the inclination of the earth's axis to its orbit would be sensibly altered. It is conceivable that there might be no material damage or loss of life whatever. The cometary nucleus may consist of such fragile stuff that it would never penetrate our protecting atmospheric shield. Instead of death and destruction, we might witness the most dazzling meteor display on record.

One thing we never need worry about is death by asphyxiation from poisonous gases released by the comet. It is true that you read of molecules such as cyanogen and carbon monoxide and other poisonous substances that have been identified in the coma and comet tail. But they are not the same molecules that cause death by inhalation on the earth. They are *fragments* of these molecules that only exist in the highly rarefied conditions found in a comet. They would immediately be rendered harmless by contact with the gases of our atmosphere.

It has been estimated that we can expect the earth to collide with a comet on the average of once every 80 million years. Your chance of colliding with an automobile is vastly better.

# What's in a comet and how do we know?

How can astronomers be so sure there are iron, hydrogen, sodium, and dozens of other chemical elements in the sun and stars?

They obtain this information by means of an instrument attached to their telescope called the spectroscope, or rather spectro*graph,* since such observations are made today either by photography or some electronic scanning device. It is hard to believe, but nevertheless true, that because of the spectograph we have a much better knowledge of the chemical constitution of the atmospheres of stars hundreds of trillions of miles away than we have about the constitution of the earth itself a few hundred miles beneath our feet. In all probability, you will never have an opportunity to work with a spectograph or even see one in your whole life. But if you want to have some glimmering of what's going on in astronomy, you should at least be aware of this powerful instrument, and what the observations obtained with it mean.

Centuries ago, men must have noticed the colors flashing from pieces of cut glass. For thousands of years they must have gazed in wonder and awe at the colors displayed by the rainbow. But the sight of these colors failed to stir their scientific curiosity. Aristotle discussed the nature of the rainbow at considerable length. He accounted for the outer red bow by a fairly plausible assumption that it originates from reflection of sunlight from numerous small particles, as when the sun is reddened by smoke and haze. His explanation for the green and blue sounds kind of forced. In fact, after reading Aristotle we prefer to believe that the rainbow is produced by the iridescent draperies of the virgin nymph Iris, sweeping across the heavens.

Nearly a thousand years later, Descartes and others speculated about the nature of light and origin of colors without producing anything that was much in advance of Aristotle. The first systematic scientific investigation of light and color may be confidently dated as 1666, when Isaac Newton, then twenty-four years old, began some experiments in optics at his home in Lincolnshire. His studies at Cambridge had been temporarily interrupted by the plague, which became so bad that the university was compelled to close for awhile. As it turned out, this plague, or Black Death, which brought death and misery to thousands, worked to Newton's advantage, as it enabled him to conduct some experiments free from academic restrictions. (Fig. 30)

Newton admitted a beam of sunlight into his darkened room through a small hole made in the "shut" of a window.

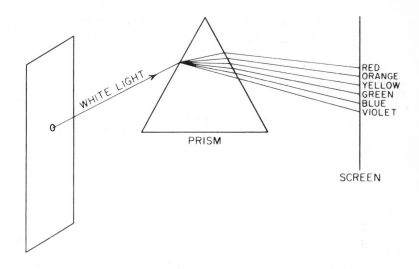

FIGURE 30. Newton's experiment with the prism. Newton
let a beam of white light pass through a hole in the shutter
into a prism. After passing through the prism, the beam was
spread out into a series of rainbow colors on the opposite wall.
(From *The Fascinating World of Astronomy* by Robert S.
Richardson, McGraw-Hill.)

The beam, after passing through a prism, fell on the opposite wall, where it formed an oblong colored strip, or spectrum. In later experiments he secured a spectrum in which
the colors were better defined by admitting the sunlight
through a slit instead of a round hole, and by using a lens
to render the diverging rays from the slit parallel before
entering the prism. In other experiments Newton placed
the lens beyond the prism at such a distance that the colors were brought to a focus on a sheet of white paper. He
does not appear to have used two lenses, one in front of
the prism and the other behind it, as we would do today.
Newton said that the slit through which the light was ad-

mitted was "but a tenth or twentieth part of an inch broad, or narrower. . . ." This is a rather important bit of information, as will appear later.

From a dozen or so experiments that Newton performed with this crude optical setup, he concluded that the beam of white sunlight must consist of a mixture of rainbow colors. These colors were made evident because the glass prism *refracted*, or bent, the various colors by different amounts, red the least and then by increasing amounts through orange, yellow, green, blue, to violet, which was bent the most. The spectrum apparently consisted of overlapping colored images of the hole or slit. Newton continued this work in optics through the next six years, before reading a paper on his experiments before the Royal Society in 1672. This famous paper, now regarded as one of the classics of science, aroused considerable comment among the members, mostly unfavorable. Although the discussion continued for years, nobody seems to have gone to the trouble of verifying Newton's results by repeating his experiments.

Nothing more of significance was done with the solar spectrum until 1802, when an English chemist, William Wollaston, performed some experiments similar to Newton's. Apparently he admitted the sunlight into his spectroscope through a narrower slit than Newton used. Wollaston found that the spectrum of the sun was not a *continuous* strip of rainbow colors as Newton thought, but was broken in seven places by narrow dark spaces or lines. For some obscure reason he failed utterly to realize their true significance, supposing the five strongest lines to mark the natural divisions among the simple colors! This is an outstanding example of a man who made a discovery of major importance in science without being able to comprehend the fact.

The dark lines were forgotten for another dozen years, until they came to the attention of a German optician, Joseph Fraunhofer, in the course of some other work. Fraunhofer was the first to study the spectrum of the sun with equipment comparable in quality to that of today. Whereas Newton never reported any dark lines in the spectrum, and Wollaston saw only seven, Fraunhofer observed and catalogued about 500. He designated the strongest by letters, determined their positions in the spectrum, and even succeeded in measuring the wave-lengths of the strongest. Fraunhofer also found that certain of these dark lines in the solar spectrum were present in the spectra of the stars. His work was of such basic importance that the dark lines in the solar spectrum are still known as the *Fraunhofer lines*. (Fig. 31).

It has always been a mystery why Newton failed to see even the strongest of the Fraunhofer lines. One very obvious reason, of course, is that his prisms and lenses were of such poor-quality glass and workmanship. Newton cautions his readers that the glass should be "free from bubbles and veins . . . with its polish elaborate" so that "there are left all over the glass a numberless company of very little convex polite risings like waves"! Besides the poor quality of his equipment, it is this writer's personal belief that he failed to see the dark lines because he used too wide a slit. When you look into a spectroscope that is in proper adjustment, the Fraunhofer lines appear black and sharply defined. Now watch what happens as you widen

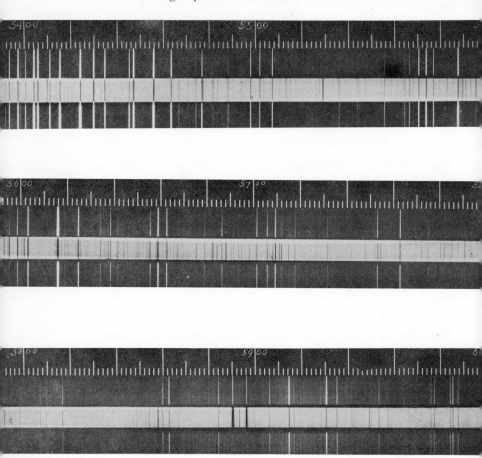

FIGURE 31. The light central strip is the spectrum of the sun broken by the dark Fraunhofer lines. The dark strip on either side is the spectrum of glowing iron vapor showing bright lines. Notice that many of the bright and dark lines match closely, proving existence of iron in the sun. The two strong dark lines in bottom strip are Fraunhofer's D lines of sodium.

the slit. The lines expand and grow blurred and faint. Newton says he used a slit width of about 1/20 of an inch. But from the description of his optical setup, calculation shows he should have used a slit width more like 1/1,000 of an inch! As it was, he might have been able to discern some of the strongest Fraunhofer lines *if he had already known they were there.* But Newton had no reason to expect such markings in the spectrum. He would not have recognized their presence unless they had been forced upon his attention.

There is another reason Newton missed the Fraunhofer lines which has been overlooked simply because it is so obvious. Newton apparently performed his optical experiments alone and unaided at his mother's home in the little village of Woolsthorpe. Working by himself, he must have experienced considerable difficulty in getting his prisms and lenses properly adjusted and lined up with the beam from the sun. If you don't believe it, get some prisms and lenses and try it sometime. Newton probably had to view the spectrum from across the room where he was holding a prism, and never had an opportunity to examine the colors at close range. If he had had a capable assistant, it seems impossible that he could have missed the Fraunhofer lines.

Skipping ahead to the latter half of the nineteenth century, physicists found that many of the *dark* lines in the spectrum of the sun and stars were at the same positions as certain of the *bright* lines produced by glowing chemicals in laboratory spectra. For example, common table salt, which is chemically known as sodium chloride, produces two bright lines in the yellow. These two bright yellow lines match (almost) exactly with the strong dark lines called Fraunhofer's $D_1$ and $D_2$\*. Now it is possible that two lines in the spectra of glowing elements familiar to us on earth might match closely with two of the thousands of dark Fraunhofer lines purely as a matter of accident. But that can hardly be the case with an element such as iron, which produces hundreds of lines practically identical with solar lines. This one-to-one correspondence between lines known to arise from the various elements on earth with lines in celestial spectra is so striking there can be no doubt as to their identity. At present, 67 of the 103 known terrestrial elements have been identified in the sun, most of them with assurance.

### THE DOPPLER-FIZEAU EFFECT

As indicated by the footnote, we had to hedge on our statement about the lines in celestial spectra matching "exactly" with those in laboratory spectra. There are always slight systematic differences between the two sets of lines (except in the case of the galaxies, for which the differences are enormous). These differences are usually so slight that you might suppose we could disregard them altogether. The agreement is close enough so that most people would probably describe it as "pretty good." But in science such small differences, especially if they are *systematic* in nature, or correspond to some definite pattern, are just the kind of thing you *don't* want to disregard. (Fig. 32)

In 1842 an Austrian physicist, Christian Doppler, dem-

---

\* Lines in the sun and stars never match identically with lines in laboratory spectra owing to the motions of the celestial bodies (Doppler effect) and other small line shifts.

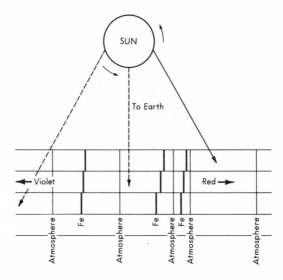

FIGURE 32. The Doppler effect illustrated by the rotation of the sun. Light from the side of sun approaching the earth shows spectrum lines shifted to violet (shortward) side relative to lines in light from center of solar disk. Light from receding side of sun shows lines shifted to red (longward). Lines originating in atmosphere of earth show no Doppler effect.

onstrated mathematically that the color of a star should undergo a change depending upon whether it is approaching or receding. Suppose the only light emitted by a star was the yellow light of the two D lines mentioned previously. If the star is receding, the result is the same as if the light waves from the D lines were slightly drawn out in length, causing them to be shifted to the red side or "longwards" of their rest positions. If the star is approaching, the observer will receive more light waves per second than if the star were at rest, causing a slight displacement "shortwards" of the lines toward the violet. (An analogous effect occurs in the case of sound waves emitted by a moving body. If a train is rapidly approaching with its horn blowing, the tone rises in pitch, then drops abruptly as the train sweeps past.) Moreover, HOW MUCH the spectrum is shifted toward the violet or red depends upon HOW FAST the star is approaching or receding. The effect postulated theoretically by Doppler was verified experimentally seven years later by Armand H. L. Fizeau, a French physicist.

By measuring the wave-lengths of lines photographed in the spectrum of a star with a *comparison spectrum* from some laboratory source, the Doppler shift of the stellar lines to the red or violet of their rest positions can be measured accurately. Notice that the Doppler shift only tells us the velocity of the star directly toward or away from us, or in our *line of sight*. It tells us nothing about the motion of the star *across* our line of sight.

# CHAPTER 11

# *The spectrograph applied to comets*

The first person to behold the spectrum of a comet was Giambattista Donati of Florence, on August 5, 1864. The comet showed three bright bands superposed on the faint spectrum of the sun. This single observation gave him considerable information at once. The faint solar spectrum evidently came from sunlight reflected by dust and other cometary debris. But the bright bands must arise from light emitted by gases in the comet itself. What were these gases? That was a question Donati was unable to answer. For a century ago practically nothing was known about the spectra of glowing gases. The laboratory spectroscopist had to catch up with the astronomical spectroscopist, or *astrophysicist*.

There was not much danger of the astrophysicists getting too far ahead where comets were concerned, at least. Observations of their spectra had to be made visually with the spectroscope, and what a frustrating job it must have been! A naked-eye comet often gives the impression of being a bright object, owing to its large size. Actually, the illumination from a large comet is far less than that of the full moon. And the illumination from the full moon is 1/500,000 that of sunlight! Yet the full moon casts strong shadows. Even the planet Venus casts distinct shadows. But there is no case on record of anyone who claimed to have seen his shadow by the light of a comet.

Few astronomers of the last century knew anything about photography, and fewer still had any knowledge of astronomical spectroscopy. Their attitude toward these innovations is exemplified in a story told about S. W. Burnham, a famous observer of visual double stars. Someone asked him if he had ever seen the D lines in the solar spectrum. "Yes, I've seen them," Burnham replied. "But I didn't think much of them."

The first photographs of the spectrum of a comet were taken in 1881 by Henry Draper in the United States and Sir William Huggins in England, both on Tebbutt's comet and both on the night of June 24. Although good spectrograms of scores of comets have been secured since that early date, none differ significantly from the one first observed visually by Donati: bright bands superposed on a faint Fraunhofer spectrum. Whereas Donati had no convenient catalogue of spectral features he could consult in searching for the origin of the bright cometary emissions, the astrophysicist today has detailed measures on laboratory spectra available for immediate comparison purposes, as well as theoretical considerations to aid him in identification. Some cometary emissions are easy to identify. Others present problems of unusual perplexity and interest.

Comets are such strange and exotic objects that we

might expect them to consist of correspondingly strange and exotic substances. On the contrary, we find in comets the same familiar elements that exist in abundance on the earth; the same elements, in fact, of which your own body is composed. But it is true that in comets these elements exist in combinations that we can only reproduce with difficulty, if at all, in the laboratory. Someone has described them as unfamiliar compounds of a few familiar elements.

What is so unusual about these molecules? Perhaps a crude illustration may help.

You are lost on the hot, barren desert. All day you have been without water. Stumbling into an abandoned shack, you discover a bottle containing some colorless liquid. The bottle bears the label $H_2O$. You assume it is water and drink it without hesitation. *But* . . . suppose the bottle bore the printed label OH. This looks as if it were the familiar symbol for the water molecule, $H_2O$, with the letters transposed and no 2 after the H. You feel that OH must surely be closely related to $H_2O$ although not identical with it. Thirsty as you are, you might hesitate a bit before trying some OH.

Table 4 contains a list of the molecules that have been

# T A B L E   4

## Molecules and atoms found in comets

Comet head: $OH, NH, CN, CH, C_3, C_2, NH_2, OH^+, CH^+$; Na, OI, Fe.

Comet tail: $CO_2^+, CO^+, N_2^+$.

Head and tail: $OH^+, CH^+$, Na, OI.

Head ("sun grazers"): Fe, Na, Ni, K, Cr, Cu, $Ca^+$. Molecules absent.

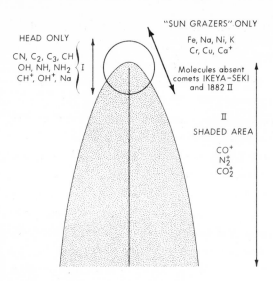

HEAD ONLY

CN, $C_2$, $C_3$, CH
OH, NH, $NH_2$
$CH^+$, $OH^+$, Na

I

"SUN GRAZERS" ONLY

Fe, Na, Ni, K
Cr, Cu, $Ca^+$

Molecules absent
comets IKEYA-SEKI
and 1882 II

II

SHADED AREA

$CO^+$
$N_2^+$
$CO_2^+$

FIGURE 33. Schematic distribution of particle emission from a comet.

identified in comets. It must be emphasized that ALL these molecules and atoms do not occur in ALL comets, or, as the table shows, even in all parts of the same comet. When a comet is nearer the sun than 0.7 A.U., or 65 million miles, the two yellow D lines of the sodium atom (Na) may appear. Lines of a few other metals may occur but only within less than about 0.5 A.U. Lines of iron (Fe) were observed in Comet 1882 II, a "sun grazer" that passed through the solar corona.

Of particular interest are the "forbidden" lines of the oxygen atom OI. Ordinarily, if an atom has the opportunity to emit a ray, it will proceed to do so without hesitating more than 1/100,000,000 of a second about it. In a hot gas, an atom is under such intense bombardment from radiation and other particles that almost immediately it is put into a suitably excited state to emit the ray again. Such emissions, occurring myriads of times per second, build up the permitted lines commonly observed in laboratory spectra.

Emission of forbidden rays is not necessarily strictly taboo but only rather unlikely. It is not often that anyone jumps off a high building but it does happen at long intervals. Atoms are so reluctant to emit forbidden rays that they may hesitate for minutes or hours before making the transition. These rays are so weak that they are only observable under especially favorable conditions.

Lines of OI in cometary spectra had been observed before but had always been attributed to emission by oxygen atoms, not in the *comet,* but in our own atmosphere. (You will also find emission from atoms of neon in a comet if you have to expose on its spectrum through the glow from a neon sign.) It is usually easy to distinguish such telluric lines from those originating in a star or comet because they show no Doppler shift: they are essentially the same as the lines recorded in the comparison spectrum. Until recently, cometary spectra were all on such a small scale that the positions of the oxygen lines could not be determined with sufficient accuracy to establish their origin. It was hard to believe that there could be enough oxygen in the cometary nucleus to produce such forbidden lines, and hence they were supposed to be atmospheric. But spectra of Comet Mrkos (1957d) and Comet Seki-Lines (1962c), taken with the powerful instrumentation of the 200-inch telescope, have revealed that the oxygen lines have the same Doppler shift as the well-known cometary emissions: proof that the oxygen belongs to the comet and not to us.

Molecules with the + sign are "ionized." In an electrically neutral molecule the total plus charges of electricity equal the total negative charges. Should a molecule or atom lose an electron, or one negative charge of electricity, the balance is upset. The particle is now electrically positive, which fact is indicated symbolically by the + sign written as a superscript.

In our desert illustration we said that the OH on the bottle looked as if it had some relation to the water molecule, $H_2O$. Looking back at the list of cometary molecules in Table 4, we find others that seem vaguely familiar, too. $NH_2$ and NH remind us of the formula for ammonia, $NH_3$, the colorless, pungent gas issuing from a bottle of smelling salts. CH might claim a kindship with methane, $CH_4$, or marsh gas. And $CO^+_2$ must be our old friend carbon dioxide ($CO_2$), the soda-water molecule, in disguise.

Stable molecules of carbon dioxide, methane, ammonia, and others are believed to exist in comets. But they may exist, not in their normal gaseous form as we know them, but as ices in the solid state. (Of course, what is "normal" depends upon where you are in the universe. "Normal" for us would seem very odd to the inhabitants of Jupiter.) The comet model we are describing here, with the solidified gases, is one proposed in 1950 by Fred L. Whipple of Harvard, which has given us a new conception of the cometary nucleus.

For more than a century astronomers had generally accepted the "sand bank" or "gravel bank" comet model, in which the nucleus was presumed to consist of a swarm of cold solid particles mostly no bigger than pebbles or grains of sand, although there might be a few masses of many tons. The particles were thought to contain occluded gases absorbed at some unspecified time in the past. Such an object beyond the orbit of Mars would be visible chiefly by reflected sunlight, and would present essentially the same appearance as an asteroid at the same distance. Then, as the comet approaches the sun the particles are warmed, and the occluded gases begin to escape, forming the coma and tail.

There would seem to be no escape from the conclusion that the nucleus must be continually losing material to the coma and tail, and once lost has little prospect of getting it back. We know, of course, from the glow of the zodiacal light that there is a considerable amount of matter in "empty" space. The comet sweeps up a portion of this material, so that some of the particles it has lost are recovered eventually. But even on the most liberal estimates of the quantity of matter between the planets, it seems impossible that a comet can pick up from space enough material to sustain itself indefinitely. Thus, the existence of a flourishing tail poses an especially difficult problem for the sand-bank model. We have historical evidence that in the last 2000 years Halley's comet has made some thirty revolutions around the sun, and Encke's comet about fifty revolutions. Yet these bodies show no indication that they are running out of gas. It is true that some comets have failed to appear at all as predicted, despite an intensive search for them. Apparently certain cometary nuclei contain a nearly inexhaustible supply of tail-making material, while others are not so well fortified in this respect.

## THE ICY-CONGLOMERATE MODEL

In Whipple's cometary model the nucleus, instead of consisting of a *swarm* of particles, is rather in the nature of a *conglomerate*. The word comes from the Latin *conglomerare*, "to form into a ball." The term as ordinarily used refers to fragmented rock cemented together by some finer-grained material. A petrologist might describe a chunk of peanut brittle as a conglomerate of peanuts bound together in a matrix of sugar and syrup. The cometary nucleus is a conglomerate of rocky fragments ranging in size from walnuts to microscopic grains cemented in a matrix of "ices," consisting of frozen molecules of water vapor, carbon dioxide, ammonia, methane, and others. As the nucleus approaches the sun and its temperature begins to rise, the ices start to evaporate, methane first, then ammonia and carbon dioxide at the distance of Mars, and water vapor at the distance of the earth. Since the nucleus is an irregular spongy mass of ice and rock, evaporation would occur at different rates over the surface. Places where evaporation is proceeding rapidly might be the source of the jets often seen issuing from the nucleus into the coma.

One of the best features of the icy-conglomerate model is that it provides a natural explanation of the puzzling changes in velocity that have been observed in certain comets, notably Encke's, d'Arrest's, and Wolf 1. As every child knows now, the velocity of a rocket in space can be altered at will by turning on its jets. The application of a similar force to the nucleus should produce the same effect on a comet. These "jets" might be the bright streams of material in the coma mentioned above. We should be careful, however, not to identify jets in a comet with jets in a rocket simply because their names are the same. The physical processes involved in the two cases may be quite different. But if a cometary jet is formed by particles ejected at high velocity, their reaction upon the nucleus would change its velocity in essentially the same way as a rocket jet.

As the comet nears the sun, the nucleus is not only warmed but its surface is exposed to the solar ultraviolet rays in greater intensity. These energetic rays are the ones that are most effective in breaking up the molecules familiar to us into fragments of molecules. If these fragmentary molecules were released at the surface of the earth, they would combine immediately with the atmosphere to form stable molecules again. Why don't they form stable combinations in the comet? On most photographs the coma gives the impression of being a thick gas cloud. But this is purely a photographic effect due to the continued action of light in building up an image on the emulsion. To show faint markings in the tail, it is necessary to overexpose the image of the coma until it is "burnt out," as the saying goes. Actually, the material surrounding the nucleus in the coma is so highly rarefied as to constitute a "hard" vacuum by ordinary standards. Collisions are such rare events that a fragmentary molecule has little chance of returning to the stable form. In space these molecules can retain their fragmentary (ethereal) form indefinitely. (Fig. 34)

But why do they *shine*? The particles are still cold, aren't they? Or at least not hot enough to be self-luminous. Gases exposed to sunlight on the earth don't shine. Why should they in a comet?

It is hard to see how a comet can have any other source of energy available to it but the sun. We believe, therefore, that solar radiation must be the answer. As their spectra show, part of comets' light is simply reflected sunlight. The light from some objects, such as Comet Peltier (1936a), is

FIGURE 34. Comet Arend-Roland, photographed May 1, 1957. Comets shine by light reflected and scattered from dust particles; also from sunlight emitted by fluorescence. During the exposure of 51 minutes the telescope was tracking the comet, so that the star images are drawn out into lines instead of appearing as points. (Lick Observatory, Mount Hamilton, California.)

practically all reflected sunlight. But the numerous bright bands are evidently produced by quite a different process from surface reflection. This process is called *fluorescence.*

Although fluorescence is not a process we meet every day, neither is it a particularly rare one. Driving at night along a dark highway, you probably have seen a ghostly glow ahead which turns out to be a signboard shining by the illumination from your headlights. Or perhaps you have gone hunting minerals with a mercury-vapor lamp. The lamp emits ultraviolet or "dark" light, but scarcely any radiation that we can see. Occasionally, a rock glows brightly when the ultraviolet radiation strikes it. Many minerals, liquids, and dyes possess this property of *emitting* visible light when illuminated by ultraviolet or "invisible" light.

Certain molecules are able to absorb energy from the radiation beyond the violet in the spectrum, of shorter wave-length than our eyes can perceive. The energy obtained from this ultraviolet radiation is immediately re-emitted by the molecules, although not necessarily in the same form as it was absorbed. Instead, the radiant energy may be emitted as light of longer wave-length that is visible to our eyes. Such a process is called *fluorescence.* When the ray emitted is the same color, or wave-length, as the ray absorbed, the process is called *resonance fluorescence.* We believe that the bright cometary emissions are produced by resonance fluorescence. An explanation of comet luminosity based on this general process was first advanced in 1911. But not until thirty years later had spectroscopic techniques been developed capable of making possible a critical comparison between observation and theory.

If the bright cometary bands arise from the absorption

and re-emission of light from the sun, then the strength of the cometary bands should correspond to the strength of the solar spectrum at these positions. Now owing to the dark Fraunhofer lines, the solar spectrum is very irregular in strength. Suppose a particular ray which a cometary molecule can absorb and emit happens to be weak in the sun. Then theory predicts it should also be weak in the comet, even though in laboratory spectra this ray ordinarily is strong. On the other hand, a ray ordinarily weak in laboratory spectra may come out abnormally intense in a comet, if the light from the sun is bright at this position.

The Doppler effect is involved in the problem in a most interesting way. (It is hard to make ANY observation in astrophysics in which the Doppler effect is not involved in *some* way.) The solar spectrum may affect a comet differently depending upon its velocity relative to the sun. Suppose that a particular cometary ray can be excited to emission only by absorption of that identical ray in the solar spectrum. But it happens that the light of this particular ray is heavily obscured by Fraunhofer lines. Then this ray will be absent or abnormally weak in the cometary spectrum. Let us say this is the situation when the comet is far away and approaching the sun with low velocity. As it nears the perihelion of its orbit, however, its velocity increases rapidly. As a consequence, the comet "sees" the sun as if the whole solar spectrum were shifted slightly shortwards toward the violet. It may happen that the Fraunhofer lines are shifted out of the way, so that the molecule is exposed to the full intensity of the solar radiation. Now a bright line appears in the spectrum of the comet that was weak or missing altogether before. Similar remarks apply if the comet is receding from the sun and the spectrum is shifted longwards toward the red. Thus the cometary bands may exhibit peculiar changes in strength as it swings around the sun.

Although we have spoken of the "light emitted by a comet," it is evident that comets, strictly speaking, are not self-luminous in the same sense as the sun and stars. A comet is wholly dependent upon the light of the sun for its luminosity. If the sun went out, the comets would all go out, too. They would still be there in space revolving in their present orbits. But so far as visibility is concerned, for us they would cease to exist.

The icy-conglomerate model gives a generally satisfactory explanation of the physical characteristics of a comet. Resonance fluorescence provides a generally satisfactory theory of a comet's luminosity. It must not be supposed, however, that the situation is completely under control and we need no longer concern ourselves over these problems. On the contrary, to borrow an expression from another field of endeavor, we have just begun to fight. It has only been since about 1958 that we have been able to secure photographs of cometary spectra on a large enough scale for detailed analysis, comparable to that in the stars. The reader should remember that progress in our knowledge of comets is often slow simply because of lack of suitable objects for study. There are always plenty of stars and nebulae to observe. But you have to catch a bright comet when you can.

# CHAPTER 12

## *Shooting stars*

If you lived in the country, far from city lights, when you were a youngster, you must remember the long summer evenings when you sat on the front porch with your friends, watching the sunset colors fade and the stars come out. Occasionally, as the twilight deepened, you would be startled by a streak of light flashing across the sky. "There goes a shooting star!" you would shout. You were always supposed to wish on a shooting star. None of my wishes on shooting stars ever came true but I continued wishing on them just the same. I never wondered why they failed to come true, or why shooting stars should have any relationship to my personal desires in the first place.

There was one thing about shooting stars, however, which I did wonder about a good deal. I would fix my attention on a group of stars. Presently a star would fall

in that part of the sky. Yet all the stars were still there!
So far as I could see, not a single one was missing. I always ended up by distrusting my observations. There *must*
have been a star I overlooked. Otherwise, where could the
shooting star have come from?

It is always a good idea to distrust your observations
and to be on the lookout for errors. But when your observations after careful checking repeatedly give the same
results, it is barely possible there may be some truth in
them. As it happened, in this case my observations were
sound enough but the conclusion I drew from them was
wrong. It was true that I saw a shooting star. It was also
true that none of the stars were missing afterward. But
was the object that fell a *star*?

We saw in Chapter 2 that the stars are huge hot bodies
similar to the sun, so far away that they do not show a
disk as the sun does, but instead appear as mere points
of light. Now you would think a man was crazy who told
you that our star, the sun, could "fall" or "shoot." It is just
as ridiculous to think that any other star could perform
such a feat. We begin to wonder if the objects we have
been calling "shooting stars" may not be bodies wholly
different from the stars.

## DISTANCES OF STARS AND
## SHOOTING STARS COMPARED

There is fortunately an easy way of settling the matter.
We said earlier that Alpha Centauri, the nearest star, is
distant 25 trillion miles, or 4.3 light years. This distance is
so tremendous that two observers on opposite sides of the

earth, about 7900 miles apart, would both see Alpha Centauri in the same direction in space. The most delicate instruments would be incapable of revealing the slightest change in its position as viewed from one station and the other. To detect a measurable displacement, it is necessary to view Alpha Centauri from opposite points on the orbit of the earth, 186 million miles apart.

But if two observers only 30 miles apart viewed a bright shooting star simultaneously, they would see it in widely different directions. One might say it flashed out in the bowl of the Big Dipper; the other would declare it first appeared at the crook in the handle. Obviously, an object cannot be very far away if a separation of only 30 miles makes such a big difference in its apparent direction in the sky. Considering how easy it is to get a rough estimate of the distance of shooting stars, it is surprising how long it took us to do it. Some 2000 years ago Hipparchus determined the length of the year with an error of only about seven minutes. But it was 1798 before any systematic measures were made on the distance of shooting stars. Between September 11 and November 4 of that year two students at Göttingen, Brandes and Benzenberg, observed from different stations 402 meteors, of which they considered 22 to be identical. They obtained an average value for their altitude of 61 miles. This must be one of the earliest scientific measures on the extent of the earth's atmosphere.

The fact that shooting stars occur in the upper atmosphere explains why astronomers prefer to call them *meteors,* from the Greek word meaning "things in the air." Meteors are only related incidentally to the science of meteorology, however, which is concerned principally with

the study of the upper atmosphere as related to the
weather.

METEORS? METEOROIDS? METEORITES?

A source of endless confusion in the study of "things in the
air" is that several words which sound almost the same
have quite different meanings. The words that cause the
most trouble are *meteor, meteoroid,* and *meteorite.*

In an effort to clarify the situation the International
Astronomical Union in 1962 published a table of "Basic
Definitions in Meteoric Astronomy," recommended by a
committee especially appointed for that purpose. It is desirable to become familiar with these terms, and since the
*Reports* of the I.A.U. are only available in a scientific library, they are given here for ready reference. We shall
simply state them first and then talk about them briefly
afterwards (except for "I," which the committee left out
for some reason).

BASIC DEFINITIONS IN
METEORIC ASTRONOMY *

A. *meteor:* in particular, the light phenomenon which re-
   results from the entry into the earth's atmosphere of
   a solid particle from space; more generally, as a noun
   or an adjective, any physical object or phenomenon associated with such an event.

* *Transactions of the International Astronomical Union,* Vol. XI A,
Reports. p. 228, Academic Press, London and New York, 1962.

B. *meteoroid:* a solid object moving in interplanetary space, of a size considerably smaller than an asteroid and considerably larger than an atom or molecule.

C. *meteorite:* any object defined under B which has reached the surface of the earth without being completely vaporized.

D. *meteoric:* the adjectival form pertaining to definitions A and B.

E. *meteoritic:* the adjectival form pertaining to definition C.

F. *fireball:* a bright meteor with luminosity which equals or exceeds that of the brightest planets.

G. *micrometeorite:* a very small meteorite or meteoritic particle with a diameter in general less than a millimeter.

H. *dust:* when used with D or E—finely divided solid matter, with particle sizes in general smaller than micrometeorites.

J. *absolute magnitude:* the stellar magnitude any meteor would have if placed in the observer's zenith at a height of 100 km (1 km = 0.6214 miles).

K. *trajectory:* the line of motion of the meteor relative to the earth, considered in three dimensions.

L. *path:* the projection of the trajectory on the celestial sphere, as seen by the observer.

M. *train:* anything (such as light or ionization) left along the trajectory of the meteor after the head of the meteor has passed.

N. *persistent:* an adjectival form for use with M indicating durations of some appreciable length.

O. *wake:* train phenomena of very short duration, in general much less than a second.

P. *radiant:* the point where the backward projection of the meteor trajectory intersects the celestial sphere.

Q. *earth-point:* the point where the forward, straight-line projection of the meteor trajectory intersects the surface of the earth.

R. *zenith attraction:* the effect of the earth's gravity on a meteoric body increasing the velocity and moving the radiant towards the zenith.

S. *orbit:* the line of motion of a meteoric body when plotted with reference to the sun as origin of coordinates.

T. *shower:* for use with A or D—a number of meteors with approximately parallel trajectories.

U. *stream:* for use with A or D—a group of meteoric bodies with nearly identical orbits.

A few words about A, B, and C, which cause the most trouble:

The "empty" space between the planets actually contains a multitude of bodies. We are not aware of them individually, as they are too small to be observable with optical telescopes. At a close approach, we can photograph asteroids down to about a mile in diameter. Bodies smaller than the smallest observable asteroid might be called *meteoroids.* The term is unfamiliar to many, although invented more than a century ago by H. A. Newton of Yale.

We do not become aware of a meteoroid unless it encounters the earth. As it rushes through the upper atmosphere, the body leaves the luminous path popularly called a "shooting star." What is the source of its luminosity? It seems reasonable to suppose that friction with the atmosphere causes the particle to glow briefly. We know from

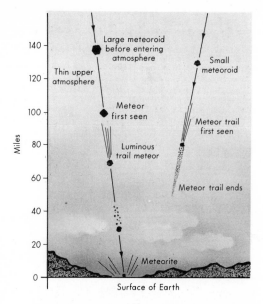

FIGURE 35. Illustrating stages in the transition from *meteoroid* to *meteor* to *meteorite*.

everyday experience that friction makes bodies hot, especially when moving rapidly. Meteoroids enter the atmosphere with velocities as high as 45 miles per second. Attractive as such a hypothesis seems, we are nevertheless compelled to reject it. A highly heated particle like a spark from a fire would not be visible at a distance of 50 or 60 miles. Actually, the source of luminosity in a meteor probably depends in a complex way upon several factors which still are only imperfectly understood. Even a "slow" meteoroid with a velocity of 8 miles per second undergoes violent collisions with the air particles along its trajectory. These collisions tear material from the surface of the meteoroid with such force that they are set in motion with velocities corresponding to a temperature of several thousand degrees. The atoms form a cloud around the meteoroid much larger than the body itself. It is the light emitted from this cloud of energized atoms that constitutes the meteor. The meteoroid cannot survive this bombardment from the air for long. Its atoms dissipate away into the atmosphere and in a moment are gone. Calculations based upon the distance and brightness of meteors show they are produced by particles of incredibly small size, usually no bigger than a kernel of wheat or a grain of sand.

It must be emphasized again that a meteor is the *visible manifestation* of a meteoroid. A meteor is nothing tangible that you can touch, or weigh, or hold in your hand. We often say, "Look at the wind!" But you don't see the *wind*. Wind is air in motion. What you see are the *effects produced by the wind:* trees swaying, clouds of dust, flying leaves, etc. Similarly, you see a meteor rather than the meteoroid.

Practically all meteoroids entering the atmosphere are tiny particles that are vaporized before penetrating to within 25 miles of the surface. Meteoroids exceeding 8 inches in diameter generally survive their fiery plunge through the atmosphere and reach the earth. These fallen remains of the meteoroids are called *meteorites*. The transition from *meteoroid* to *meteor* to *meteorite* is illustrated in Figure 35.

# *Your fireball*
# *observation*

The best visual observations of meteors cannot approach the accuracy now attainable as a matter of routine by photographic and radio techniques. But there is one type of meteoric object for which visual observations are still supreme—the fireball. For information on the flight of a fireball we are wholly dependent upon what people *see*. A fireball is a spectacular object that bursts forth without warning and is gone in a few seconds. The problem is to determine its path. Everybody knows how widely people will disagree in describing an event that happened right in front of them, such as an auto accident. It is not surprising, therefore, that reports on a fireball not only disagree but often are flatly contradictory. It frequently happens that witnesses are unable to render a useful report simply for lack of a suitable vocabulary. This explains why one good "fix" by a trained observer may be worth a dozen "erratics" by individuals who are long on enthusiasm but short on perception. This is unfortunate, because the knowledge necessary to make a useful observation is easily acquired, and is applicable not merely to fireballs but to any object in the sky.

First we are going to give a sample of how NOT to report a fireball. The following is a not-too-imaginary conversation between a meteoriticist and an important on-the-spot witness to a fireball that went soaring over his alfalfa patch.

METEORITICIST: "Now what would be your estimate of the apparent size of this fireball?"

WITNESS: "Well, sir, I'd say she was just about the size of a dishpan."

METEORITICIST: "I see. Er . . . where was the fireball when closest to you?"

WITNESS: "Right square overhead."

METEORITICIST: "Where did the fireball first appear?"

WITNESS: "Well . . . it was in the south, kind of over a little bit toward the west."

WITNESS's WIFE (suddenly breaking in): "Now, Homer, it wasn't toward the west at all. It was more over toward the east."

WITNESS (after a pause): "Yes, I guess it was more toward the east."

Let us examine these remarks.

The statement that the fireball appeared to be about the size of a dishpan has no meaning, not even for the witness. If he had said, ". . . the size of a dishpan *as seen from the distance of one mile*," it *would* have had some meaning. But since very few people have had much experience in viewing dishpans at different distances, their judgment on such a matter is not likely to be very trustworthy. "Overhead," although a respectable term, is one that has to be taken with reservation. Experienced interviewers know that people will say an object was "overhead" if it was more than halfway from the horizon to the zenith. And finally, how far to the west is "a little bit toward the west"? We let such expressions pass in casual conversation. But in science we must use words that have a definite meaning to everyone.

## SIZE IN THE SKY

A woman can take one look at another woman and a month later give you a detailed description of everything she had on. Women can be good observers. Yet this same woman might be incapable of describing some object she saw in the sky. It all depends upon whether the observer is prepared in advance and knows what she is talking about. But the technical terminology used for describing some object in the sky is really much simpler than the expressions used in dressmaking, such as "gored down the middle," "shirred across the front," etc.

Distances in the sky are not described in terms of dishpans, dinner plates, teacups, and other household utensils, but in *angles*. An angle is the difference in direction between two lines drawn from a common point. Angles are most commonly expressed in degrees (°), minutes ('), and seconds ("), of arc. The angular distance measured around a circle is divided into 360 equal parts (degrees), written 360°. Each degree is divided into 60', and each minute into 60". The number 360 seems to be of very ancient origin, chosen long ago when people believed the sun moved eastward each day by 1/360 part of the whole distance around the heavens. (Accurately, the sun moves 1/365.25636 of a whole revolution on the average per day.) Angles of various sizes are shown in Figure 36.

To estimate angular distances in the sky quickly and with fair accuracy, you should already have a mental picture of the angular, or apparent, separation between some familiar celestial objects. For estimating small angles there is only one choice—the full moon. The full moon, besides

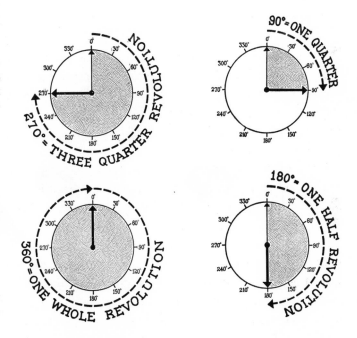

FIGURE 36. How angles are measured. The difference in direction between the two arrows tells the number of degrees through which the moving pointer has turned. (From *A Brief Text in Astronomy* by Skilling and Richardson, Holt-Dryden, rev. ed., 1959.)

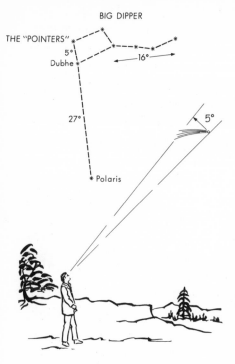

BIG DIPPER

THE "POINTERS"

5°

Dubhe

16°

27°

5°

* Polaris

FIGURE 37. The observer sees a bright meteor which appears to be about the same angular length as the stars between the "Pointers" of the Big Dipper. Since the man only sees the length of the meteor projected against sky, it appears shorter than its real length.

being a familiar sight to everyone, has the advantage of being almost exactly half a degree, $0°.5$, in diameter. Therefore, if you should see a persistent meteor train, try to estimate its length in full moons. An estimate of five full moons, for instance, would mean an apparent length of $5 \times 0°.5 = 2°.5$. If an object has the width of half the full moon, its angular diameter is $0°.25$. For estimating larger angles, the two stars in the end of the bowl of the Big Dipper are separated by $5°$. The length of the handle of the Big Dipper is $16°$. The distance between Polaris and Dubhe, the star at the top end of the bowl of the Big Dipper, is $27°$. (Fig. 37)

## ANGULAR DIAMETER AND
## LINEAR DIAMETER

The fact that the two stars in the end of the bowl of the Big Dipper are separated by 5° tells us nothing about their distance apart in miles or light years. Neither does it tell us anything about their distance. If the size of an object is wholly unknown, it is impossible to tell anything about its distance without additional information. This is hard to explain to people who give you a detailed account of the exact size and distance of some light they saw in the sky the other night.

If we know the angular diameter of an object and its distance, however, we can immediately find its linear diameter, or "real" size. In fact, if we know any *two* of the *three* quantities—angular diameter, linear diameter, and distance—we can always find the third, from the following simple equations:

1.  $A° = $ angular diameter (degrees) $= 57.3 \dfrac{L}{D}$

2.  $L \phantom{°} = $ linear diameter $\phantom{xxxxxx} = \dfrac{A° \times D}{57.3}$

3.  $D \phantom{°} = $ distance $\phantom{xxxxxxxxxx} = \dfrac{57.3\,L}{A°}$

It is important to notice that the distance of the object, D, and its linear diameter, L, must both be expressed in the same terms. It makes no difference whether these are feet, inches, hectometers, or light years, provided both are the *same*. A few examples will illustrate the use of the formulae.

a. The head of a comet has an angular diameter of $0°3$. The distance of the comet from the earth is known to be 21 million miles. What is the linear diameter of the comet's head?

We are given $A = 0°3$, $D = 21,000,000$ miles, and we are to find L. Using equation 2, we have:

$$L = \frac{21,000,000 \times 0.3}{57.3} = 109,900 \text{ miles}$$

b. A dishpan 2 feet in diameter is viewed from a distance of 0.5 miles. What is the angular diameter of the dishpan?

To solve this problem we use equation 1. But first we must either change the size of the dishpan to miles, or its distance to feet. In this case, it seems easier to change miles to feet. Since 1 mile = 5,280 feet, 0.5 miles = 2,640 feet. Now we can write:

$$A° = \frac{57.3 \times 2}{2,640} = 0°0434$$

Thus the dishpan would appear to be slightly smaller than 1/10 the size of the full moon.

c. A balloon 40 feet in diameter has an angular diameter of $3°$. What is its distance?

We are given $L = 40$ feet, $A = 3°$, and must find $D$, using equation 3.

$$D = \frac{57.3 \times 40}{3} = 764 \text{ feet}$$

## "HE WENT THATAWAY"

To specify directions in the sky we need terms with a definite significance, rather than such vague expressions as "a little toward the east" or "kind of in the south."

Looking at the sky on a clear dark night, we often have the feeling of being at the center of a huge *celestial sphere*, with the stars set on its inner surface. This sphere is always rotating, carrying the stars and other celestial objects with it from east to west. We are only able to see the half of the celestial sphere that projects above the *visible horizon*.

The point on the celestial sphere directly overhead is the *zenith*. Opposite the zenith, directly underfoot and hence out of sight on the invisible part of the celestial sphere, is the *nadir*. We noted earlier that the point "overhead" is not so easy to determine. Pick out some star that seems to be in your zenith. Now face in the opposite direction and locate the zenith again. The result may surprise you. To locate the zenith accurately, surveyors use a small weight suspended by a thread, called a *plumb line*. The plumb line, when extended indefinitely upward, pierces the celestial sphere in the zenith; extended indefinitely downward, in the nadir. Although we speak of the zenith and nadir as if they were points on the celestial sphere, they are actually directions in space, like the vernal equinox. Names such as "zenith" and "nadir," as well as others we shall use, have a strange sound because they come from the Arabic.

The visible horizon is an irregular line that is useless for exact measurements. We therefore create an ideally perfect horizon by imagining a circle drawn around the celestial sphere midway between the zenith and nadir. This is the *astronomical horizon*. If you were lying on a raft far out in the ocean, your visible and astronomical horizons would be almost identical.

We tell "how high" an object is in the sky by its *altitude*. This is the angular distance measured vertically upward from the horizon to the object. (Henceforth when we speak of the "horizon" it will always be the astronomical horizon.) The distance from horizon to zenith is one-quarter of a whole revolution around the celestial sphere, or 90°. A star when rising or setting has an altitude of about 0°. The altitude of a star one-third of the way from horizon to zenith is 30°. If halfway to the zenith, its altitude is 45°. The altitude of a star at the zenith must be 90°. We can also speak of the "altitudes" of objects below the horizon by using negative angles. A little before sunrise the altitude of the sun is −1°. The altitude of an object halfway between horizon and nadir is −45°. (Fig. 38)

Altitude alone is not enough to fix the position of an object upon the celestial sphere. We not only need to know "how high." We must also know "which way." We tell the direction of an object by its *azimuth*. Azimuth is the angular distance measured from the north or south point on the horizon, around the horizon clockwise toward the right, to the point where a line drawn from the zenith through the object meets the horizon. Suppose we measure azimuth from the north point. Then if you stand facing north you are looking in the direction of azimuth 0°. Your right hand, extended to the east, points toward azimuth 90°. Your back is toward 180°. Your left hand, extended, points toward azimuth 270°. Continuing on, you return to the north point in azimuth 360°, or 0°. Navigators and

FIGURE 38. Illustrating how altitude and azimuth are measured. Here azimuth is shown as measured from south point on horizon, as is customary among astrono- mers. Navigators measure azimuth from north point. (From *A Brief Text in Astronomy* by Skilling and Richardson, Holt-Dryden, rev. ed., 1959.)

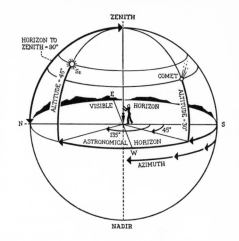

surveyors reckon azimuth from the north point, astronomers usually from the south point. Always be sure to specify which point is used.

(In accurate work, azimuth has to be found from observations of a north polar star, usually Polaris, with a surveyor's transit instrument. Methods of making such observations are described in books on practical astronomy.)

Surveyors are the only people who are in the habit of carrying a plumb line and transit instrument around with them. When making a hasty eye estimate of the altitude and azimuth of an object, we have to do the best we can without instrumental aids. Most people know the approximate direction of the compass points in their neighborhood. In any case, don't worry about which way is north and east, but try to fix the position of the object relative to some well-defined landmark, such as a chimney or church steeple. Be sure also that you carefully note your own position at the moment, if your observation is to mean anything.

If the object is fairly low in the sky, say, with an altitude of less than 30°, you can estimate its azimuth with considerable assurance. The greater its altitude, the more uncertain its azimuth becomes. Eye estimates for altitudes exceeding 60° are of little value.

## TO FIND A FIREBALL

Let us see how our knowledge of altitude and azimuth can be used to furnish information on a fireball. In case you happen to witness one of these spectacular objects, instead of gazing at it open-mouthed, try to observe the following:

1. Time of appearance. (Noted later.)
2. Altitude and azimuth of point of appearance.
3. Altitude and azimuth of point last seen.
4. Color and brightness.
5. Sound, if any.
6. Smoke trail, if any, and its duration.
7. Behavior of the fireball near end of its path. Did it sputter or break up?

This sounds like a pretty big order. But it is not particularly difficult to note and remember these things if you have already anticipated them, so that you do the right things automatically without having to review them in your mind. As soon as possible, make a written record of what you saw, putting down everything that might be of significance. *Don't trust your memory.* A week or month later the event will have changed in your mind.

The information most desired is the azimuth of the point of disappearance, or the "end point." If reliable reports are available from several widely separated stations, the point of fall, and possibly the meteorite itself, can be located. But if the reports are vague and contradictory, the area of search becomes so large that the prospect of finding the remains, if any, becomes very slim indeed. A circle 10 miles in radius may not look very big on a map. But it looks enormous when you are standing in the center of it.

Figure 39 shows in principle how the trajectory of a fireball can be determined from two observations of its altitude and azimuth. Two observers situated 25 miles apart at A and B see a fireball appear simultaneously at F. A sees it in the direction of the line AF; B in the direction of BF. Notice that a *single* observation only puts the fireball at some point along the observer's line of sight. To locate the fireball it is necessary to determine the place where the two lines of sight intersect.

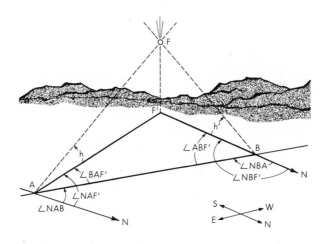

FIGURE 39.   Illustrating principle of how altitude of meteor might be determined by two observers.

The distance AB between the stations is accurately known. Each observer has previously measured the bearing or direction of the other station from the north point. That is, A sees the station at B in the direction of ∠ NAB; B sees the station at A in the direction of ∠ NBA.

Let F′ mark the spot on the ground directly beneath the fireball at F. Then measuring always from the north, A sees F′ in the direction of ∠ NAF′; B sees F′ in the direction ∠ NBF′. Then in the plane triangle ABF′ we know:

$$AB = 25 \text{ miles}$$
$$\angle A = \angle NAF' - \angle NAB$$
$$\angle B = \angle NBF' - \angle NBA$$

and so from trigonometry we can calculate the distances AF′ and BF′.

If A measures the altitude of the fireball, h, and now knows AF′, he can calculate its distance above the surface, F′F. B can do the same with his altitude, h′, and his knowledge of BF′. Both values obtained for F′F should agree —which they will not. But *how closely* they agree provides a check on the accuracy of their measures.

In practice, conditions naturally depart widely from this ideal situation. Yet if reports are available from half a dozen or so reliable sources, it is rather surprising what consistent results can be obtained from them.

# CHAPTER 14

## *Meteor showers*

If conditions for observing meteors are favorable—clear sky, no moon, no artificial illumination—you can expect to count about three or four during the course of an hour's watch. On certain nights, however, your count will be much higher, perhaps twenty or fifty per hour. Such occasions occur when we have a meteor "shower." The term is misleading, as it arouses a mental picture of meteors pouring from the sky like water out of a sprinkler. Once or twice a century there may be a display that justifies such a term. Most showers, however, are a dismal disappointment to the general public, which is often led by the newspapers to expect something spectacular.

One of the most magnificent showers on record occurred early on the morning of November 12, 1833, when stars began falling "as thick as snow coming down in a snow storm." Several observers noticed that there was a

FIGURE 40. The meteor shower on the morning of November 12, 1833. The meteors seemed as if radiating from the constellation of Leo.

definite pattern to their motion. They did not fly across the sky at random, but radiated from a point in the constellation of Leo in such numbers as to make the sky in that direction resemble an umbrella. The meteors continued

until dawn, and since Leo at that time was nearly overhead, most people had the impression that the meteors
came from the zenith. More careful observers noticed that
the point of radiation remained fixed in Leo, and moved
along with the stars at the same rate as the celestial sphere.
Recognition of this point, called the *radiant,* was one of the
most notable astronomical discoveries of the nineteenth
century.

The shower of 1833 was noteworthy also for the fact
that it compelled astronomers for the first time to pay some
attention to meteors. Previously, they had generally regarded these "shooting stars" as too trivial a phenomenon
to be worthy of serious study. But the November meteors,
or "Leonids," put on such an impressive performance they
could no longer be ignored. And so astronomers began ask-
ing, had there been brilliant showers like this before?
Would they occur again? What were these objects? How
did they originate?

Investigation revealed that the shower of 1833 was not
a unique event by any means, although few had been so
spectacular. Unfortunately, many accounts of these showers had been written by individuals whose chief interest
was not in science, but in trying to terrify the people into
repentance for their numerous sins. Often it was hard to
tell what *did* happen.

A striking exception was Alexander von Humboldt's
description of the meteor shower of 1799. Humboldt was a
writer-scientist-explorer of immense reputation in the
eighteenth and nineteenth centuries. Furthermore, he believed in getting his information firsthand rather than out
of somebody else's book in the library. In the fall of 1799
Humboldt was in Cumaná, a settlement on the northern

coast of Venezuela. Judging from his diary, his stay there was not lacking in incident. On October 27 he had an encounter with a "Zambo," a native of bellicose disposition who attacked him with a club in one hand and a knife in the other (although most of the natives were friendly and peaceful). The next day he was busily occupied observing an eclipse of the sun. On November 4 a violent thunderstorm came up suddenly. In addition to a powerful electrical explosion, the village was rocked by two earthquake shocks, and for several days afterward the sky was darkened by a peculiar red vapor. Then on the morning of November 12 came the great meteor shower.

Humboldt tells us that about 2:30 A.M. the most extraordinary, luminous meteors began rising out of the sky from the east and northeast. Soon there was not a space in the heavens equal to three full moons which was not filled with bolides and falling stars. The meteors left luminous traces that often lasted from seven to eight seconds. Many of the shooting stars had a nucleus as large as Jupiter, from which darted sparks of vivid light. The display gradually ceased after four o'clock, although some falling stars could still be detected for fifteen minutes after sunrise.

During the shower of 1833 many people in the United States became terrified, convinced that the Day of Judgement was at hand. Humboldt remarks anent the shower of 1799, "Almost all the inhabitants of Cumaná witnessed these phenomena, because they had left their houses before four o'clock, to attend early morning mass. They did not behold these bolides with indifference; the oldest among them remembered that the great earthquakes of 1766 were preceded by similar phenomena."

It seemed incredible that two such rare and extraordinary events as the brilliant meteor showers of 1799 and 1833 could have occurred on exactly the same date simply by chance. The records showed there had been weak showers from November 11 to 14 for several years before the great display of 1833. H. A. Newton of Yale succeeded in tracing the November meteors back to A.D. 902; only then they had not been the "November" meteors, but the "October" meteors. From his researches he concluded that the showers are produced by a swarm of particles revolving around the sun in a period of thirty-three years, in an orbit extending from the orbit of the earth to slightly beyond the orbit of Uranus. The earth intersects this orbit every year about November 12. The particles are thinly distributed around the entire orbit, so that there is a weak shower regularly about this date. But the distribution is uneven and especially strong at one place in the orbit, so that when the earth encounters this main swarm we have brilliant showers, such as those of 1799 and 1833. The fact that brilliant showers do not occur regularly every thirty-three years was explained by the disturbing action of Jupiter, Saturn, and Uranus.

There were good Leonid showers in 1866 and 1867, although not as impressive as that of 1833. Great expectations for a major shower were aroused when the next thirty-three-year cycle came around in 1899. The public seems to have been unduly stimulated by the considerable number of Leonids that fell the year before on November 14. People were accustomed to the reliability of astronomers when it came to predicting eclipses of the sun and moon, and confidently expected them to display the same uncanny accuracy on meteor showers. (The fact that a few astronomers expressed doubt about meeting the main swarm passed almost unheeded in the general excitement.) Unfortunately for the reputation of astronomers, meteors were conspicuous chiefly by their absence on the expected date. There was no use trying to explain to the public that predicting a meteor shower was quite a different proposition from predicting an eclipse. The meteors were supposed to fall and they didn't fall. The Leonid shower of 1932 was not exceptional, nor was that of the one recently passed in 1965.

We were about ready to give up hope on the Leonids, when they put on a spectacular display on the morning of November 17, 1966, which from early reports rivaled the great shower of 1833. According to one eyewitness, "It seemed like there were thousands of meteors. They were falling so fast you couldn't count them. Some of them lighted up the whole sky, leaving great big tails of white smoke and streamers behind them." This description reminds us of Humboldt's account of the shower of 1799.

One of the finest showers that has occurred so far this century was the Draconid shower of October 9, 1946, best seen on the West Coast of the United States about an hour after sunset. Although visibility was reduced by the full moon, some observers reported a count of a meteor per second. (My count was about a dozen per minute. Somehow, meteors never fall so fast for me.) The shower reached its maximum between 7:30 and 8:00, and by nine o'clock conditions had returned to normal.

There is no need for meteors to be falling "as thick as snowflakes" to locate the radiant. The position of the radiant can be determined with considerable accuracy from a count of only a dozen or so per hour. Figure 41 shows the

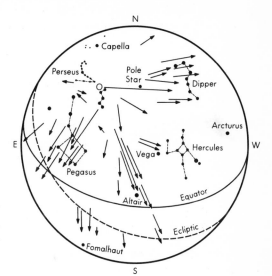

**FIGURE 41.** Sketch showing some of the Perseid meteors. Although made by two inexperienced observers, the radiant was easily determined.

trails on a rough sketch recorded by a husband-and-wife team during two hours of watching on a hazy night in August, on the occasion of the Perseid shower. Although the husband was a professional astronomer, neither he nor his wife was an experienced meteor watcher. If you had been out of doors that night you probably would have noticed that meteors were rather plentiful, although it would never have occurred to you that a "shower" was in progress. Even less evident was the fact that the meteors had a definite flight plan. But if you had plotted the meteor paths on a star chart, a pattern would have begun to emerge very early. Inspection of the chart shows that the meteor paths when prolonged backward intersect within an area smaller than the disk of the full moon. A few meteors have paths that fall far outside the radiant. These are "sporadics," or meteors not associated with the shower. But there are reasons for believing that all meteors belong, or once belonged, to some shower.

WHY THE RADIANT?

Why do meteors appear to radiate from a certain point among the stars as if they were being created there by spontaneous generation?

The radiant is entirely an effect of perspective. Radiants are all around you on the earth, only you are seldom aware of them unless you are an artist or architect or someone whose eye is trained to notice such effects. In some cases, however, the effect is so conspicuous that it forces itself upon your attention. Looking down a long straight stretch of railroad track, the rails appear to be diverging from a point in the distance. Of course, you are not deceived for an instant. You know the rails are not diverging but are parallel to each other. You have also seen the effect many times driving along a highway. But when you see meteors flashing out of the sky, you have no experience to guide you. The meteors certainly *look* as if they

FIGURE 42.   Illustrating how the radiant is an effect of perspective.

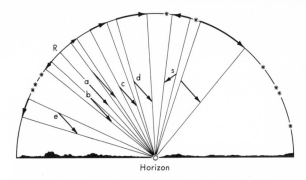

FIGURE 43. The radiant is an effect due to perspective. The meteors are moving through space in parallel lines. When seen projected against the celestial sphere, they seem to be radiating from point at R.

were diverging from a point in the sky. So you think they *are* diverging, or radiating, from a certain point in the sky.

The true motions of the meteors are shown in Figure 43. The stars are at immense distances; the meteors only a few miles away. Yet so far as *appearances* go, both stars and meteors seem to be at the same distance on the celestial sphere. The particles in the swarm enter the atmosphere moving together along parallel lines. The observer at O becomes aware of them by their bright paths in the atmosphere. He sees these paths foreshortened by projection against the celestial sphere. A meteor moving directly toward him, as at *a*, would appear merely as a bright point at the radiant. Meteors seen a little farther away, as at *b* and *c*, would show short paths. Meteors viewed still farther from the direction of the radiant, as at *d* and *e*, would show long paths. At *s* we see a sporadic, or nonshower, meteor, whose path shows no relationship to the others.

# CHAPTER 15

---

# *Meteor velocities*

The Perseid and Leonid meteors are described as "swift," whereas the Draconids are said to be "slow." Why should meteors from one constellation move any faster than those from another?

The particular mythological figure which happens to contain the radiant is of no significance. What *is* significant is the way the meteor stream encounters the earth. Does it overtake the earth? Or does it meet the earth head-on?

Consider first an encounter in which a meteoroid overtakes the earth. We shall represent velocities by arrows. The *length* of the arrow shows the *speed* of motion. The *head* of the arrow shows the *direction* of the motion. A quantity such as velocity, which has both magnitude and direction, is called a *vector*.

In Figure 44 the observer on the earth at O feels that he is motionless in space and that the bodies around him are doing all the moving. Hence he is unaware of the orbital velocity of the earth of 18.5 miles per second, indicated by the arrow OE. We can reproduce his isolated outlook on the universe by an arrow OE', equal in length to OE but oppositely directed. If we apply this fictitious velocity to the observer, we must also apply it to the meteoroid. Suppose the meteoroid has a velocity relative to the sun, represented by OM, of speed 22.5 miles per second. The result is the same AS IF the meteoroid struck the motionless earth with a velocity of 22.5 − 18.5 = 4.0 miles per second. Suppose the meteoroid had collided head-on with the earth. Now the result would be the same as if the meteoroid had struck the motionless earth with a velocity of 22.5 + 18.5 = 41.0 miles per second. In the first case we would have a "slow" meteor; in the second, a "fast" meteor.

These particular examples are so easy that we can solve them almost by intuition. But a meteoroid will seldom be so accommodating as to meet the earth directly from in front or behind. In the more general case, we can always get the solution by making use of a proposition from mechanics.

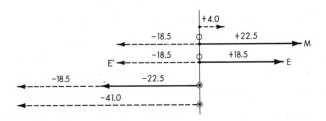

FIGURE 44.   Illustrating how meteors appear "fast" or "slow," depending upon how they encounter the earth.

A body at O is acted upon by a force which in a certain time would cause it to move from O to A. (Fig. 45) Simultaneously the body is acted upon by another force which in the same time would cause it to move from O to B. It can be demonstrated that the two forces acting together would cause the body to undergo the displacement represented by OC. The point C is found by completing the parallelogram which has OA and OB for adjacent sides, and then drawing the diagonal OC. OC is the *resultant* of OA and OB.

Let us apply this method of handling velocities to an encounter between the earth, Draconids, and Leonids. (Fig. 46) The orbital velocity of the Draconids at encounter of 24.2 miles per second is represented by OD. As before, the orbital velocity of the earth of 18.5 miles per second is indicated by OE. (Fig. 47) Again it is convenient to simulate the observer's apparently motionless state by the fictitious velocity OE'. At the moment of collision we can regard the meteoroid as undergoing the two displacements OD and OE'. To the observer the meteor will seem to be moving along the resultant, OD', of OE' and OD, with a speed of 12.6 miles per second. As we would expect, this apparent speed of the meteor is less than its true speed,

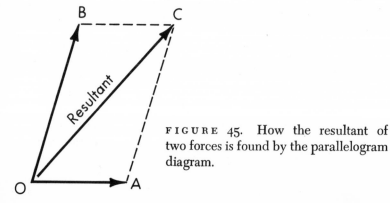

FIGURE 45. How the resultant of two forces is found by the parallelogram diagram.

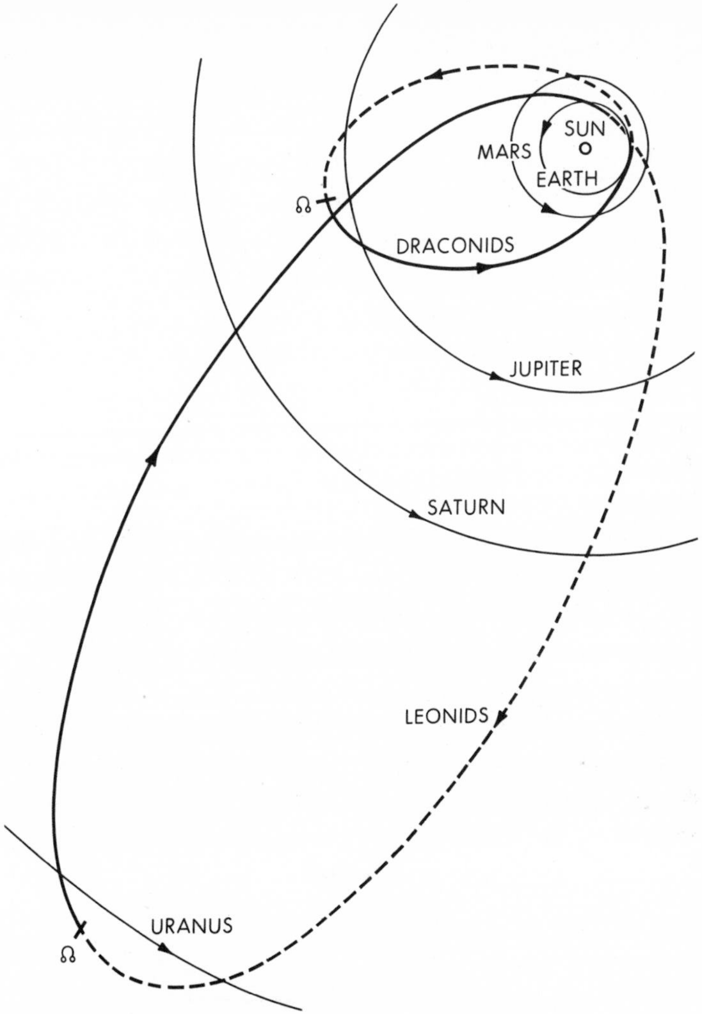

FIGURE 46. Orbits of the Draconid and Leonid meteors. The Draconids are moving in the same general direction as the earth and appear to us as "slow." The Leonids, which we meet nearly head-on, appear to us as "fast." Broken lines indicate section of orbits below plane of diagram.

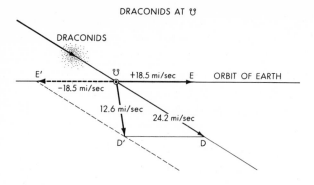

FIGURE 47.  Encounter between the earth and Draconids.

since the Draconids overtake the earth. Hence, the Draconids are "slow."

What is the situation when the earth meets the Leonids? The orbital velocity of the Leonids of 25.8 miles per second combines with the fictitious velocity of 18.5 miles per second of the earth to give the resultant OL'. Now the velocity of the Leonids at the moment of encounter exceeds that of the Draconids by only 1.6 miles per second.

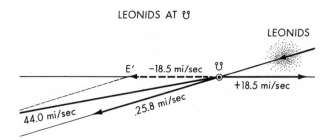

FIGURE 48.  Encounter between the earth and Leonids.

Yet they appear to be moving 31.4 miles per second faster, with a velocity of 44.0 miles per second, since our encounter is in the nature of a head-on collision.

In practice, we have to work the problem the other way around. We measure the apparent velocity of the meteor and then combine this with the known velocity of the earth to obtain the meteor's true velocity. We also have to make allowance for the gravitational attraction of the earth. As the meteoroid approaches the earth its motion is changed both in speed and direction. The effect of the earth's attraction on the shower is always to increase the altitude of the radiant, or give it a displacement higher in the sky toward the zenith, whence the name of this effect—"zenith attraction." There is also a small correction for the velocity of rotation of the earth.

MEASURING METEOR VELOCITIES

In 1867 the U.S. Naval Observatory stationed observers at Richmond, Virginia, and Washington, D.C., 97 miles apart, to study the Leonid shower of November 13. Their measures showed that bright meteors first become visible at an altitude of about 75 miles and disappear at about 55 miles. Measures on the altitude of meteors by modern techniques give values of approximately 70 miles and 35 miles. Thus the crude visual measures of a century ago yielded results in fair agreement with those of today.

It is not so with meteor velocities. Meteors dart out of the sky and vanish with such rapidity that it is impossible by the eye alone to determine their velocities with an accuracy approaching that of other astronomical measures. It must have been obvious to every worker in this field that the ideal way to measure meteor velocities was by photography. But the prospect, a hundred years ago, for making such measures was not exactly encouraging. The first telescopic picture of a star was taken on the night of July 16–17, 1850, when J. A. Whipple succeeded in photographing Vega with the 15-inch refractor of the Harvard College Observatory. The exposure time was 100 seconds on this fourth-brightest star in the sky. This photographic feat was not in any sense a "break-through." In fact, it was hardly more than a slight dent in man's assault upon the heavens. Little progress in stellar photography was possible until the advent of the dry plate about 1870. If photographing a bright *fixed* star was a major problem, what hope was there of photographing a *shooting* star?

Yet as early as 1860, J. Homer Lane not only advocated meteor photography but suggested placing a rotating bicycle wheel in front of the camera to interrupt the exposures for velocity measures, essentially the same scheme used today. Lane was an amazingly versatile thinker. Besides contributing the rotating bicycle wheel to meteorics, he was the first to publish a paper on the distribution of temperature within a star.* It was in this paper that he announced the famous paradox known as Lane's law, that the more heat a star radiates the hotter it gets.

The first systematic two-camera program of meteor photography was begun in 1894 by W. L. Elkin of Yale, and carried on by him until 1909. In 1899 he adopted Lane's idea of placing a rotating wheel in front of the camera to interrupt the exposure at regular intervals. It

---

* *American Journal of Science and Arts*, Series 2, Vol. 4, 1870, p. 57.

is hard to assess Elkin's work, as he published so little during his lifetime. Apparently he overestimated the accuracy with which he could determine meteor velocities with his equipment, for an analysis of his measures made after his death showed that the base lines he used, of 2 and 3 miles, were too short to give reliable results. Nevertheless, to Elkin should go the credit of pioneering in a field that for several decades was kept alive chiefly by amateurs.

In 1936 Fred L. Whipple of Harvard began a photographic meteor-observing program with cameras placed 24 miles apart. After the war, the program was resumed on a larger scale in New Mexico, with cameras of special design by James G. Baker. Since this is intended as a book about comets and meteors rather than methods of observing them, we will only say here that the cameras are exceptionally fast, with an effective focal ratio of F/0.85, and a field 53° wide. The meteors are recorded on film through a rotating variable-speed shutter which interrupts the exposures from ten to sixty times a second, as desired. With two such cameras 25 miles apart, the altitude and velocity of a meteor can be determined with an accuracy, not of a few miles, but of a few feet!

RADIO METHODS

Photographic and visual observations of meteors of necessity depend upon the light received from them. If clouds are in the way there is no light received and hence no meteors observed. (It is astonishing the number of people who believe that clouds are no obstacle to observations with a telescope!) A century or even half a century ago, who could have dreamed that meteors could be observed even through clouds, by day as well as night, by the radiation we send to *them?* Yet that is the principle upon which observations of meteors by radio methods is based.

Electromagnetic pulses are beamed into space from a radar transmitter. As a particle rushes through the upper atmosphere it forms a long train of ionized, or electrified, air particles. The meteoroid itself is far too small to be observed. What we observe is the long column of ionized particles formed by collisions with the meteoroid. This column is vastly larger than the object that produces it, perhaps a few yards in width at first, but expanding rapidly so that within a few seconds it has attained a diameter of half a mile or more. Electromagnetic waves from the radar transmitter, encountering such a train of ionized particles, set the electrons into vibration. The vibrating electrons emit waves which are picked up and recorded by a receiver at the same station that originally emitted the pulses. Knowing the time elapsed between the instant a pulse was transmitted and received, and the velocity of light, the distance to the meteor can be determined.

# CHAPTER 16

## *To observe meteors*

Meteor observations, as already emphasized, should be made as far from artificial light as possible, where your view of the sky is not hedged in by trees and houses. A clear view of the horizon is not so important, since your observations will be mostly confined to altitudes greater than 20°. Plan your observing program for dates about five nights before and after new moon, when illumination from moonlight will not interfere. Most calendars give the dates of the new moon, first quarter, full moon, and last quarter.

If you are completely without experience, you might begin by simply counting meteors. Don't do this by strolling outdoors, taking a casual look at the sky, and then deciding meteors aren't very active tonight. Keep a systematic written record of everything you do in a large hard-cover notebook. The pages can be ruled into columns with headings such as the date, the time when you began and ended observations, the time each meteor appeared, its serial number for that night, brightness, color, and anything else about it that seems worthy of special mention. Be sure to note the observing conditions, whether the sky is clear, hazy, considerable moonlight, etc. Making observations and recording them will be easier and the time will go faster if you can find some congenial and enthusiastic person for a partner. It is good practice to spell each other at intervals of about thirty minutes, one person recording and the other observing. Initials of both observer and recorder should always be on file, so you will know whom to blame afterward, if for no other reason.

Evening is the most convenient observing time for most people, but whenever possible you should try to get in some morning hours. After having accumulated some morning and evening observations extending over several months, compare your hourly counts before and after midnight. You will probably be surprised to find that your counts for the morning hours are considerably the larger, perhaps two, three, or four times larger. This is not what you had expected, as often you were not very alert in the morning and had an uneasy feeling that you missed quite a few. Yet your records indicate just the opposite.

The explanation should be clear from Figure 49. For simplicity, suppose that all the meteoroids in our path are moving either directly toward us or directly away from us. *Before* midnight we are riding on the *back* side of the earth in its orbit around the sun, whereas *after* midnight we are on the *front* or *advancing* side. After midnight the only meteoroids escaping collision are those ahead of the earth moving in the same direction with velocities exceeding 18.5 miles per second, such as *a*. All others we will either

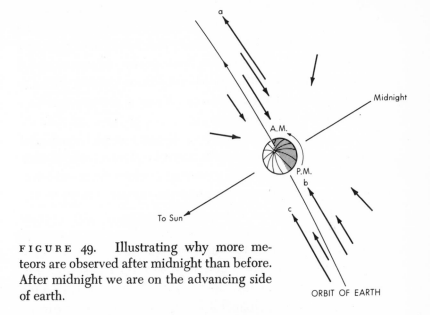

FIGURE 49. Illustrating why more meteors are observed after midnight than before. After midnight we are on the advancing side of earth.

overtake or meet head-on. But before midnight, when we are on the back side, the only meteoroids we encounter are those with velocities high enough to overtake the earth, such as *b* and *c*. Therefore, on the average, morning meteors appear faster, hotter, and brighter than those we see in the evening.

You will soon become dissatisfied with merely counting meteors and feel an urge for observations of a more challenging nature. In that case you can try your skill at determining the paths of meteors on the celestial sphere. Some observers find a ruler helps in fixing the position of a trail. The instant you see a meteor, hold the straight edge of the ruler at arm's length along its path. Estimate the points where the meteor appeared and disappeared, and its position relative to the stars nearby. Now draw an arrow at this position on your star chart equal in length to the meteor's path. Needless to say, this requires a thorough knowledge of the stars as they appear on the celestial sphere, and the ability to identify them quickly with the stars on the map. (Experts can locate a meteor trail on a map in less than a minute.)*

If a shower is in progress, at the end of a couple of hours you may have recorded several dozen trails of various lengths. These trails extended backward should intersect in a point at the position of the radiant. Owing to the errors in your observations the trails will intersect, not in a point, but at various points within the area of a small circle. The extent of this area will serve as an indication of the accuracy of your work. If you could put several full moons into the radiant, your observations need sharpening up. The few trails that fall far outside the radiant can be ignored, as they were formed by meteors that are not members of the shower. This *graphical* method of locating the position of the radiant is the, simplest and involves no mathematics.

---

* For accurate meteor plotting star maps on a gnomonic or stereographic projection should be used.

# CHAPTER 17

# Meteor swarms
# and comets

We saw in Chapter 8 that to predict the position of a body in the solar system we must know the six independent quantities, or *elements*, that determine its orbit and its position in the orbit. This information is usually obtained from (1) observations of the object's direction in space, or position on the celestial sphere, and (2) the times when it had those positions. Three observations are the bare minimum necessary to furnish the six bits of information required. You *can* squeeze by with less, but then you must make some special assumption about the orbit—that it is a circle or parabola, for instance.

Now how are we going to get three observations on a swarm of meteoroids? We can't see them in space. We can only see the multitude of flashes over the sky when the swarm encounters the earth. What can we do with *them?*

Of course, there is no law that says an orbit *has* to be based upon three or more observations of position. Orbits have commonly been worked up in this way because there was nothing but position we could observe about a body. In theory, the orbit of a body is completely determined if we know its position and velocity at any time. In this case, however, "position" does not mean merely its direction on the celestial sphere, but its location in the three-dimensional space around the sun. And "velocity" refers to its velocities in those three dimensions.

The very fact that a meteor shower is in progress gives us half the information we need right away. For it tells us the position of the swarm immediately: it is the same as that of the earth. (And of course we always know where *we* are at any moment!) Now if we knew the velocity of the meteoroids composing the swarm, we would have the whole orbit. That was the hard part—getting an accurate value for the velocity. It was the case of a problem being solved in theory but not in practice. Astronomers of the last century had to do the best they could with what they had, and their success was often astonishing.

Giovanni Virginio Schiaparelli is remembered today chiefly for his discovery of the canals of Mars in 1877. It is not taking anything away from this great observer when we venture the opinion that he probably couldn't help discovering the canals. It is our experience that you can either see the canals or you can't see them. If you or I had been looking through his telescope that night we might have discovered them, too. Actually, Schiaparelli's best work was the discovery ten years earlier of the relationship between comets and meteor showers, for which he was awarded the gold medal of the Royal Astronomical Society. Thus Schiaparelli's reputation as one of the foremost astronomers of Europe was established long before his discovery of the canals.

In 1867 Schiaparelli announced an orbit for the Leonids based upon the position of the radiant at the shower of November 13, 1866. From their appearances in the past, he derived a period for the swarm of 33.25 years. By a coincidence, Urbain J. J. Leverrier, whose calculations led to the discovery of Neptune in 1845, presented a solution of the same problem to the French Academy of Sciences on January 21, 1867. By another coincidence, Oppolzer of Vienna published at this time an orbit for a faint comet discovered by Tempel in 1865. (Leverrier's life was filled with coincidences. By a coincidence John Couch Adams almost beat him to the discovery of Neptune.) Neither Leverrier nor Oppolzer knew what the other was doing. Their astonishment can be imagined when Leverrier's orbit for the Leonids was found to be practically identical with Oppolzer's orbit for Tempel's comet. Conceivably, two or maybe even three of the six orbital elements might show a family resemblance as a matter of accident. But it was hard to believe that all six could be in such close agreement accidentally. Here are the elements as they were originally published. The reader can judge for himself.

| Orbital elements | Tempel's comet | Leonids |
|---|---|---|
| Period of revolution | 33.18 yrs | 33.25 yrs |
| Eccentricity | 0.9054 | 0.9044 |
| Perihelion distance | 0.9765 | 0.9890 |
| Inclination | 162° 42′ | 165° 19′ |
| Longitude of node | 51° 26′ | 51° 18′ |
| Longitude of perihelion | 42° 24′ | Near node |

It now developed that Schiaparelli had recently made the same discovery about the orbits of the August meteors, or Perseids, and comet 1862 III. Apparently he had obtained this result prior to the discovery of the similarity between the orbits of the Leonids and Tempel's comet, although he did not announce his findings until afterward. To Schiaparelli, therefore, should go the honor of being the first to discover the relationship between a meteor shower and a comet. The maximum of the Perseid shower occurs each year about August 10, beginning soon after midnight. This is a reliable shower during which you may expect to count as many as fifty meteors per hour if conditions are favorable. The Perseids put on about the same display year after year, indicating that the material is strewn evenly around their orbit, instead of being concentrated here and there as in the case of the Leonids.

These discoveries stimulated interest in meteorics, a field which until recently has never attracted many professional workers. By the end of the century a large amount of factual information had accumulated on meteors, mostly gathered by hard-working amateurs. It appeared that meteor showers, far from being rare events, were actually of common occurrence. According to W. F. Denning, an experienced British observer, there are about fifty showers active every night! Many radiants have been tentatively identified with comets whose orbits pass near the earth. After a century, however, we know of only about a dozen comets for which identification with major meteor showers is certain. Conversely, there are some major meteor showers that cannot be related to any known comet.

## METEOR SHOWERS AND METEORITES

You would think that the best time to look for freshly fallen meteorites would be while a brilliant shower is in progress.

It seems reasonable to suppose that when a horde of particles is entering the atmosphere there should be a few large enough to reach the surface. The chief weakness of this hypothesis is the total lack of evidence to support it. No meteorites are known to have fallen during the great showers of 1799 and 1833. You are in no more danger of being hit by a meteorite during a brilliant shower than at any other time.

That certain meteoric swarms are moving in the same orbits as certain comets, however, cannot be doubted. Do the particles in the swarm come from the disruption of the comet? There is considerable evidence to support such a hypothesis. We know from direct observation that comets often undergo such violent internal changes that they can scarcely be recognized from one week to the next, or even one night to the next. Occasionally a comet splits, the classic example being Biela's at its return in 1845. In November and December of that year there was nothing unusual in its appearance. The following January it separated into two distinct parts of unequal brightness, which went on their way as a double or twin comet. The separation of the two comets was about 200,000 miles, or slightly less than the distance between the earth and moon. At the comet's (or comets'?) next return in 1852, the two components had drawn apart by about 1,500,000 miles. Just to complicate matters for observers, the two kept alternating in brightness, so there was no way of deciding which was the "principal" comet. The pair passed out of view in September 1852 and has never been seen since.

We have an image of the cometary nucleus as consisting originally of a few large bodies several miles in diameter. As they revolve around the sun these bodies experience disruptive forces that tear them apart, and this process is repeated until eventually the entire nucleus is reduced to a loose swarm of fine particles, a sand bank or gravel bank hurtling through space. Particles are continually being lost from the nucleus, so that in the course of time the entire orbit is strewn with debris. If the orbit crosses the orbit of the earth, there will be a meteor shower every year when the earth passes through the stream.

Most of the cometary debris consists of such tiny particles that they vanish in the upper atmosphere as meteors. But there are a few big ones that reach the surface as meteorites. Meteors come from small meteoroids. Meteorites come from large meteoroids. Otherwise, there is no essential difference between them.

The foregoing hypothesis sounds so eminently reasonable, it is hard to see how anyone can doubt it. Yet meteoriticists have now come around to just the opposite point of view. They believe that the bodies which produce meteors have nothing in common with the bodies that produce meteorites. On what evidence is this belief based?

Hand a person a meteorite and what do you hear? "It's so heavy!" he exclaims immediately. What he really means is that the meteorite is so heavy *for its size*. Material of this kind, such as lead, gold, and most metals, is said to have a "high density." It is convenient to express densities in terms of some common substance, such as water. The density of a substance so expressed is called its "specific gravity." This is what the filling-station attendant means when he inquires, "What gravity oil do you want?" or when he remarks that "the gravity of your battery is down pretty low." The solution in your battery, when fully charged, has a specific gravity of 1.28, meaning that it is 28 per cent heavier than pure water. The liquid element mercury has a specific gravity of 13.6, which tells you at once that a bottle full of mercury would weigh 13.6 times as much as the same bottle full of water. Ice has a specific gravity of 0.9, so that volume for volume ice is 10 per cent lighter than water, which explains why it floats.

Certain meteorites called *siderites* have a specific gravity of nearly 8, which is about twice that of any rock you are likely to find in the vicinity. As you would expect, siderites consist mostly of metals, especially iron, nickel, and cobalt. Hence, a siderite feels about twice as heavy as an ordinary rock of the same size.

How about the specific gravity of the bodies that produce meteors?

Our knowledge on this subject is naturally limited, since of necessity we are compelled to do all our studying at long range. Evidence so far obtained from measures on the velocity and brightness of some meteors indicates that they arise from very lightweight stuff, having a specific gravity of 0.05, only 1/20 that of water. They appear to be bodies "so fragile that a block a foot or two in height would crush under its own weight at normal gravity." A substance of such extreme delicacy is consistent with the icy-conglomerate comet model in which the nucleus is presumed to consist of particles having little structural stability held together by frozen gases. If this be the case, it is easy to understand why no meteorite has certainly been known to fall during a major shower. Such flimsy material could never survive its tumultuous journey through the atmosphere.

Meteorites are now believed to have nothing to do with comets, but to be bodies which originated independently in some sort of catastrophe among masses of planetary size.

What could it have been? Collisions among the asteroids? Masses chipped off the moon by meteoroids? Fragments from an exploded planet? To answer this question we may first have to find the answer to the question of the origin of the solar system itself.

# CHAPTER 18

# Comets across the sun

One bit of information on comets of particular value would be direct observational evidence on the size of the nucleus. Such information might be obtained from a comet in transit. A clear view of the nucleus silhouetted against the disk of the sun would give us the diameter immediately, since the distance of the comet would be known from its orbit. Unfortunately, transits of comets are about as rare as transits of Venus. The last transit of Venus was in 1882, and there will be no more until June 8, 2004, and June 6, 2012. The only genuine cometary transits of which we are aware were in 1882 and 1910. Transits of Venus can be confidently predicted centuries in advance. But nobody knows when to expect a comet that will come between earth and sun.

Although these transits were noteworthy events in the history of cometary exploration, they are scarcely mentioned in most books. They provide us with some valuable information, not only on astronomy, but on astronomers, as well.

As early as 1908 astronomers knew that Halley's comet would be seen near the sun about the middle of May 1910 but until its orbit was better determined it was impossible to predict whether a transit would occur. By January of 1910, however, there was no more doubt about it. Ingress, the moment when the comet would enter onto the disk of the sun, was set at 1910 May 19, $03^h$ $39^m$ $37^s$ Greenwich Civil Time (GCT).* It was too bad that Halley's comet could not have made it a little sooner, for the transit would not occur until the sun had already set over the United States and Western Europe, where most of the big observatories were located. The sun would be splendidly situated for observation over Manchuria and the Great Sandy Desert of Australia. But who would be there to observe it?

If the West Coast of the United States had extended another thousand miles or so into the Pacific Ocean, at least the beginning of the transit would have been visible from the Lick Observatory and Mount Wilson, two of the largest in the world at that time. As it stood . . . but wait a minute! In a sense the United States *did* extend quite a ways into the ocean. For 2200 miles southwest of California lay the recently annexed territory of Hawaii, with a governor appointed by the President. Although Hawaii had no astronomical observatory, it was only a week away by steamship from San Francisco. With a celestial event coming up that might not occur again for a thousand years,

---

* The reader who tries to investigate this transit for himself may get into difficulties over dates and times. The reason is that after 1925 each day was decreed to begin twelve hours earlier than before.

it was unthinkable to let it pass unnoticed. The Comet Committee of the Astronomical and Astrophysical Society of America believed that this was no time to stand idly by on the sidelines. If there was no observatory on Hawaii, it would send an astronomer to *put* one there. A makeshift observatory was better than no observatory at all.

The astronomer selected for this big one-man expedition was Ferdinand Ellerman, of the staff of the Mount Wilson Solar Observatory, as it was called in those days. Ellerman had been with George Ellery Hale, founder of the observatory, from its beginning in 1904 on Mount Wilson, a peak of the San Gabriel Mountains overlooking the city of Pasadena, about a mile below. Actually, their association had begun in 1892, when Ellerman at the age of twenty-three had worked with Hale at his private observatory in Kenwood, a suburb of Chicago. In 1910 Ellerman at forty-one was one of the few astronomers in the United States with a solid background in all forms of celestial photography.

When I first knew Ellerman he was sixty-two, and it is hard for me to picture him as a much younger man. He had a Vandyke beard and looked exactly the way an astronomer is supposed to look. This beard was evidently an early acquisition, as it appears in an advanced stage of development in a photograph taken in 1908. Ellerman had a habit of leaving little admonitory notes around the premises. If you found a pencil with KEEP ME SHARP carved on the side, there was never any doubt about who put it there. As a solar man, he scorned to light his pipe with a match when the sun was shining, always igniting the tobacco with a burning glass. The crack of a rifle echoing over the mountain in the morning meant that Ellerman was riding the bucket to the top of the 150-foot sun tower, taking a shot at a squirrel on the way. Sometimes he would fix you with one eye in a way that I always found strangely unnerving. Not until years later did I discover that this was due to his glass eye, which had a tendency to get out of alignment.

Ellerman planned not only to observe the transit from Hawaii but also to secure photographs of the comet in April and May, when it would be a morning object in the eastern sky. For visual observing he had a 6.4-inch refracting telescope, equatorially mounted and clock-driven, borrowed up north from the Lick Observatory, and a 6-inch portrait lens for photography. Before the instruments were packed for shipping, they were given a thorough overhauling in the machine shop of the observatory in Pasadena. When an astronomer is operating far from his home base, it is advisable to try to anticipate every kind of trouble that might conceivably develop.

There is no record available of the amount of money that was poured into this expedition to Hawaii, but it is doubtful if the budget exceeded a couple of thousand dollars. It all sounds very small-time compared with our present giant science projects, with their multi-million-dollar appropriations and group research teams. But I wonder if science is as much fun today as it was half a century ago. Most astronomers worked alone and knew how to handle practically any problem that might come up. I know exactly what Ellerman would have done if he had found the cross hairs broken in his micrometer eyepiece. He wouldn't have stood around waiting for some technician to fix it for him. He would have scouted around until he found a spider web and repaired it himself. If he couldn't find a spider web he would have used unwaxed dental floss.

Ellerman left San Francisco on March 22, and after an uneventful trip reached Honolulu on the twenty-eighth. Conditions looked anything but promising. The sky was overcast with heavy clouds. He soon discovered that the weather in Hawaii was quite different from that in Southern California. Often the sun would be shining brightly in one spot while it was pouring down rain a few miles away. For his observatory he chose a site on Diamond Head where he had a clear view of the sky toward the east. Another advantage was that it was only a mile from the end of the electric car line. As he discovered later, however, the cars quit running after midnight. He solved the transportation problem by renting a motorcycle.

Much more serious was the lack of running water near the observatory site. An astronomer likes to look at a plate as soon as he has finished an exposure, so he can take it over again if anything went wrong. This is especially desirable when working on a new program under strange conditions. But since there was no water, Ellerman had to take his plates back to his cottage in Honolulu and develop them in the bathroom. Trying to process plates under such conditions must have been an ordeal, especially in the warm, moist climate of Honolulu.

It was late in April before Ellerman had his instruments set up and adjusted, after which clouds prevented observations. Finally, on the morning of the twenty-fifth the clouds disappeared, and the sky remained clear right up to the day before the transit. When he awoke on the morning of May 18 the clouds were back in force again, dark and forbidding. The sky was overcast all morning and into the early afternoon. By three o'clock he must have begun to feel some uneasiness, with ingress only 100 minutes away. Then the cloud layer began to break up, and by 3:30 the sun was shining in a clear sky.

You often hear scientists today complain that they have to spend so much time filling out progress reports that they have no time left for work. Ellerman's account of his transit observation was a masterpiece of brevity. He got it all into one sentence. "The definition of the sun most of the time was good and the granulation * came out very distinct, but no trace of the comet in transit was detected or suspected." (Fig. 50)

Figure 51 shows the sun as it appeared at the Mount Wilson Observatory on May 18, 1910, about twelve hours before ingress. The predicted path of Halley's comet is indicated by the arrow. Although 1910 was a year of low sunspot activity, there were two small groups of spots on the disk that day. Suppose the cometary nucleus to consist of a single solid mass with an apparent diameter equal to 1/10 that of the smaller spot near the center of the disk. At the distance of Halley's comet when in transit of 15 million miles, the angular diameter of the nucleus would be 3."2, corresponding to a linear diameter of 233 miles. Under fairly favorable seeing conditions, such an object would have been almost impossible to miss.

A solid object viewed against the solar disk should be much easier to detect than a sunspot of the same apparent size. Although a spot looks black on the sun, actually it is intensely bright, with a temperature of around 8000°F.

---

* The granulations are light and dark patches on the solar surface, not distinctly visible unless the seeing is fairly good. Hence, the visibility of the granulations provides a good criterion of observing conditions.

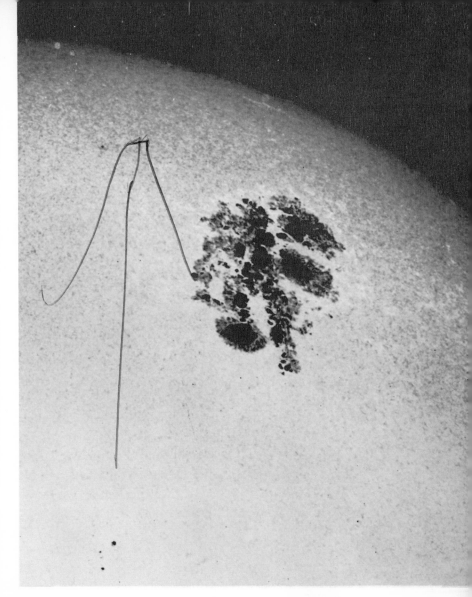

FIGURE 50. A huge spot group near edge of the sun. The mottled surface of the sun is produced by the "granulations," which become more conspicuous at the edge. (Mount Wilson and Palomar Observatories.)

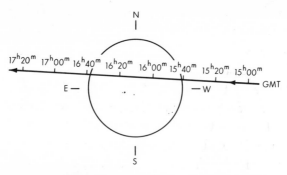

**FIGURE 51.** Photograph of sun taken at Mount Wilson Observatory on morning of transit of Halley's comet across disk, May 18, 1910. The arrow indicates path across disk of comet, which was not visible from Mount Wilson. (Mount Wilson and Palomar Observatories.)

(Fig. 50, p. 181) It only appears dark in contrast to the rest of the sun, which is at a temperature of 11,000°F. But an opaque object should look "blacker" against the disk than a sunspot. Furthermore, the reality of any suspicious dark marking could be easily verified by noting whether it was moving or not. It seems unlikely that the nucleus of Halley's comet could have exceeded 100 miles in diameter. Reports from other observers over the world were also negative: nobody could see the comet in transit.

## TRANSIT OF THE GREAT COMET OF 1882 II

Although Halley's is the most famous comet, owing to its reappearance about every seventy-six years, there are many others that have exceeded it in brightness. The only comet besides Halley's that is known to have transited the sun is 1882 II, better known as the "great" comet of 1882.

Several others *may* have made a transit, but their orbits
were not determined with sufficient accuracy so that we
can be sure about it.

1882 II became so bright it was easily visible in full
daylight. Or at least it *would* have been visible if the persistent cloud bank that hung over Europe and the United
States had gotten out of the way. Fortunately, the comet
was also observable south of the equator, but there were
so few observatories south of the equator. Out of a total
of 265 astronomical observatories listed in the *American
Ephemeris* for 1900, only 16 were in the southern hemi-
sphere. By good luck, fine seeing conditions prevailed on
the day of the transit at one of the largest of these, the
Cape Observatory in South Africa.

Ingress at this station was scheduled for late afternoon
of Sunday, September 17. Two astronomers using different
telescopes followed the comet right up to the edge of the
sun. And then it vanished! Although both observers knew
exactly where to look, neither was able to discern the nucleus against the disk. This observation is of exceptional
importance, inasmuch as it was based upon the testimony
of two trained men working under identical seeing conditions.

The puzzling thing about the transit was the extraor-
dinarily large difference between the predicted time of
ingress and the observed time. 1882 II had been well
observed, so that its orbit and motion were accurately
known. Yet according to this orbit, the comet was far behind schedule. At the observed time of ingress it should
already have been a third of the way to the center of the
disk. Now when theory and observation disagree, the
observations are always assumed to be right. It would
appear, therefore, that the orbit was not as accurate as

had been supposed, and should be differentially corrected to bring prediction and observation into agreement—were it not for the fact that an observation made twenty hours later at another observatory showed 1882 II right on schedule!

What is the explanation?

There is no "explanation." But there is plenty of speculation. 1882 II was a sun grazer that came within 300,000 miles of the solar surface at the perihelion of its orbit. This is so close that the comet penetrated the corona, the pearly halo of light that flashes out around the sun at the instant of total eclipse. Soon after passing perihelion, the nucleus was transformed from an oval into a bright line with several distinct condensations along its length. About October 9 a nebulous mass developed beside 1882 II and accompanied it through space as a satellite comet. Eventually, the comet split up into four parts, which continued out into space in approximately the same orbits. Calculations of their periods show that if still intact we might see the individual members of this foursome in 2546, 2651, 2757, and 2841.

Several other comets are known to be moving in orbits practically identical with 1882 II, notably 1668, 1843 I, 1880 I, 1887 I, 1945g, and Pereyra (1963e). The latest member of this group to pass our way was Ikeya-Seki of 1965, to be described later.

ASTRONOMERS TORN APART

Astronomers as well as comets are subject to stress and strain. A European astronomer, M. de Fonvielle, was verg-

ing upon disruption as he chafed under the clouds that
hid 1882 II from his view. It was maddening to have a
daylight comet in the sky without being able to see it.
If the clouds ever cleared away, the comet would probably
be gone, too. Finally, in desperation, he requisitioned a
balloon and prepared to go aloft. But at the last moment,
fearing his eyesight might not be equal to the occasion, he
yielded his place to a daring associate, M. Maurice Mallet.
After M. Mallet had been briefed on observing the comet
should the venture succeed, the balloon was released, and
he disappeared into the overlying gloom. He penetrated
the cloud layer and, although his efforts were badly ham-
pered by the small size of the basket, was able to make a
sketch of the comet and measure its distance from the sun.
The Mallet–de Fonvielle flight has the distinction of being
the first and only balloon ascension ever made for the express purpose of observing a comet.

---

# *The question mark beyond Jupiter–1925 II*

At first sight P/1925 II seems to be completely deficient in all those features that make a comet interesting and exciting. (Fig. 52) It is never visible to the unaided eye. It has no tail. It doesn't move in an elongated cigar-shaped orbit. And so far no one has tried to hold it responsible for the numerous disasters that have befallen the earth since its discovery. But it has some other things going for it.

The comet that we now call 1925 II was found on a photograph taken November 15, 1927, by A. Schwassmann and A. Wachmann of the Bergedorf Observatory, Germany. It certainly looked innocent enough on the discovery plate: a nucleus of magnitude 14 surrounded by a coma. A star of magnitude 6 is about the faintest you can see. Magnitudes become *larger* as stars become *fainter,* a change of 1 in magnitude corresponding to a change of 2.5 in luminosity. That is, a star just beyond the range of the eye, of seventh magnitude, is 2.5 times as faint as a sixth-magnitude star; a star of eighth magnitude, 6.25 times fainter, etc. There is an old joke that sounds pretty good the first time you hear it, that magnitudes are like your golf score: the bigger the magnitude the weaker the star. Thus, an object of fourteenth magnitude would be about 1600 times fainter than the faintest stars you can see.

The object at discovery had the characteristic appearance of a comet far out from the sun. Normally, as the comet approaches the sun it brightens up under the increasing intensity of the solar rays. About the time it reaches the orbit of Mars it begins to sprout that supposedly essential appendage of every comet—a tail. (But again it must be emphasized that some comets are no re-

FIGURE 52. Comet Schwassmann-Wachmann 1 (1925 II) as photographed on October 26, 1959, when magnitude 17.5. (Official U.S. Navy photograph, Flagstaff Station.)

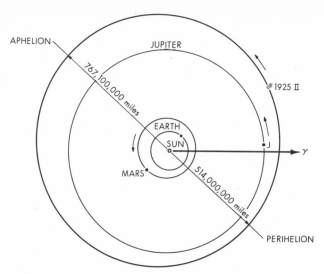

FIGURE 53. The orbit of P/1925 II at discovery on November 15, 1927.

specters of the rules. Comet Wirtanen, 1957 VI, had a short, faint tail when almost 5 A.U. from the sun, or three times the distance of Mars.) A bright comet may exhibit peculiarly shaped forms in the head, called by various descriptive terms, such as jets, fans, envelopes, hoods, and halos.

In the case of 1925 II, however, it soon became evident that here was a comet that would never come near the sun. For computations showed it was moving in an ellipse of low eccentricity with a perihelion distance of 5.5 A.U., or 514 million miles. (Fig. 53) Thus, at that time its motion was entirely outside the orbit of Jupiter. It is necessary to insert the qualifying phrase "at that time," for the orbit has since been considerably altered by the disturbing attraction of Jupiter. (Figs. 54, 55) By 1979 the comet will be

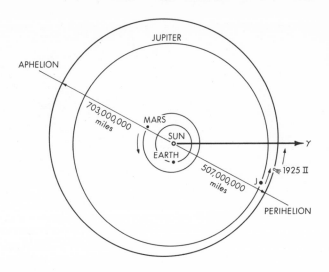

FIGURE 54.   Close approach of Jupiter and P/1925 II on June 22, 1974.

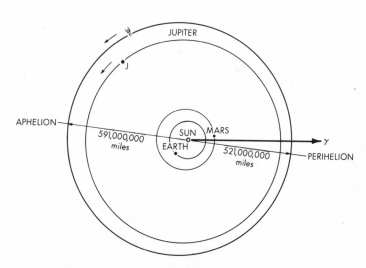

FIGURE 55.   By 1979 P/1925 II will be moving in an orbit scarcely distinguishable from a circle.

FIGURE 56.   A flare-up of P/1925 II in 1961. (Official U.S. Navy photograph, Flagstaff Station.)

moving in an orbit scarcely distinguishable from a circle, never receding from the sun by more than 591 million miles or approaching within less than 521 million miles.

Two weeks after discovery, 1925 II had fallen in brightness by two magnitudes, and by February, 1928, had dropped to magnitude 17. Then it brightened up a little to 16.5.* These changes, however, were only a feeble indication of what this comet was capable of doing. Of the many flare-ups of 1925 II, only a few will be cited of exceptional interest.

Early in January 1946, Dr. G. Van Biesbroeck, a veteran astronomer at the Yerkes Observatory, found the comet about magnitude 18. By January 25 it was up to 10.2, and on the next night he called it 9.4—which meant that in only a couple of weeks it had brightened up by 8.6

* Cometary magnitudes are often unreliable.

magnitudes, corresponding to nearly a 3000-fold increase in luminosity.

But why? Why would a little chunk of matter far out in the cold of space suddenly brighten up several hundred or thousand times? What is its source of energy? Does it come from within the comet or without? Whatever the source may be, it is still active. On October 12, 1961, a thirty-minute exposure revealed no trace of the comet on a photograph taken at the U.S. Naval Observatory, Flagstaff Station. When next observed, on October 15, the comet was recognized visually at once. Reports early in 1965 showed continued activity.

An early hypothesis ascribes the outbursts to emanations from some energetic source on the sun, such as a large spot group. This idea is an old stand-by for explaining any effect in the solar system that can't be explained in a better way. Over the years the sunspot hypothesis receives just enough support to keep it alive.

Consider the case of the flare-up that occurred in February 1946. Early in 1946 an enormous group of spots was on the sun, the second largest in recorded solar history. This spot group would have been visible to an observer on the comet from January 26 to February 8, although out of sight from the position of the earth. (Fig. 57) The diagram shows the positions of the earth during this interval. (The comet moves so slowly that it may be regarded as fixed during this short interval.) The fact that the comet underwent a major flare-up when exposed to this huge spot group was a hopeful indication that some cause-and-effect relationship existed. A dozen or so such coincidences would give us considerable confidence in a hypothesis of cometary outbursts triggered by solar emission. Unfortu-

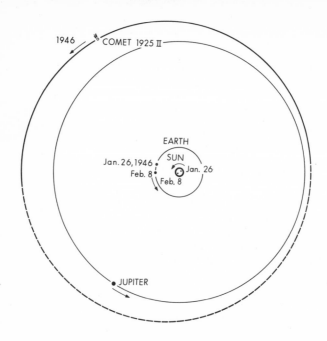

FIGURE 57. A possible explanation of flare-up of P/1925 II by radiation from giant sunspot group of Jan.–Feb., 1946.

nately for such a hypothesis, 1925 II has also flared up when nothing unusual could be observed on the sun. Furthermore, if the sun can provoke outbursts in 1925 II, why can't it exert a similar stimulating effect on other comets?

Another hypothesis attributes the outbursts to explosive chemical reactions. By postulating a suitable mixture of stable and unstable compounds, it is possible to make out a fairly plausible case for violent chemical reactions excited (again) by solar particle emission. But as the proponents of this idea themselves admit, highly specialized conditions are necessary to produce an explosion of any kind, and it is hard to believe they could exist on such an unlikely body as a comet.

1925 II is not alone in exhibiting anomalous effects. In January 1957 the nucleus of Comet Wirtanen underwent disruption when about 4.9 A.U. from the sun. It is possible to fix the date of the event within only a few days. A collision has been suggested as the most likely possibility. But 4.9 A.U. is beyond the zone of the ordinary type of asteroids. Larger asteroids than the average, called the Trojans, however, are known to revolve at about the distance of Jupiter. (They are called "Trojans" since they have been named after the heroes of the Trojan War.) Although a collision cannot be ruled out, it is a kind of desperation hypothesis, a hypothesis of last resort, to be invoked only when all else fails.

IS IT ANTI-MATTER?

Since none of the "reasonable" hypotheses hold forth much promise, let us take a plunge into the deep end and present one that borders on pure fantasy.

Could P/1925 II consist of anti-matter?

Anti-matter is what the name signifies: a form of matter opposite in structure from "ordinary" matter. This book, your body, everything around you, in fact, consists of ordinary matter. This matter is composed of atoms having a positively charged nucleus of protons and uncharged neutrons enveloped in a cloud of negatively charged electrons. Anti-matter would consist of atoms having nuclei of anti-protons and anti-neutrons surrounded by a cloud of positrons. The existence of anti-matter was postulated from theory in 1928 by P. A. M. Dirac, and such particles have since been verified from experiment. Anti-matter may exist in large quantities—not in our part of the universe, but in regions far removed from us. So far as appearances are concerned, anti-matter would be indistinguishable from ordinary matter. If brought in contact, however, both would undergo immediate annihilation, with the spontaneous release of radiant energy.

Suppose—just suppose—that P/1925 II consists of anti-matter. How did such alien corn get into the solar system? We don't know. But here it is—odd man in a totally hostile environment.

The body is under continual bombardment from meteoroids. In the atomic bomb, only a small fraction of the mass involved is converted into radiant energy. The reaction between ordinary matter and anti-matter is more efficient. ALL the matter involved is converted into energy.

Most of the meteorites striking 1925 II would be too small to produce an observable effect at the distance of the earth. But occasionally a larger one would score a hit, resulting in an explosion of such monstrous proportions as to be easily observable. The debris would subside. A period of uneasy quiet would follow—until the next one hit.

The anti-matter hypothesis has several attractive features. There is no need to postulate a tie-in with solar activity. The collisions would occur at random, as the outbursts are observed to do. Between collisions the nucleus would hardly be distinguishable from an asteroid, which is essentially the way it does look. If we assume the nucleus to have the same reflecting properties as the surface of the planet Mercury, calculations show its diameter would have to be 37 miles to appear as magnitude 18 when nearest the earth. This is nearly the same average size as the Trojan asteroids.

A body of anti-matter could not survive for long within the solar system. Soon it must all dissolve into radiation. The nuclear blasts would react upon the nucleus by changing its direction of motion, just as the course of a rocket is altered by turning on its jets. In this connection, it is worth noting that a recent analysis of the observed positions of 1925 II reveals several discontinuities in its motion.

Until more factual information becomes available, there is little point in speculating about the nature of 1925 II. It would seem that observations of the comet's spectrum at an outburst should give us just the information we want. Owing to the irregular character of the outbursts, it is extremely difficult to catch one at the critical moment. Several spectra have been obtained, however, shortly after an outburst. They showed only the reflection spectrum of the sun, indicating that the bright material surrounding the nucleus consists chiefly of dust.

Following the spectacular success of the Mariner IV encounter with Mars in July 1965, our space planners in a burst of enthusiasm issued a schedule for the forthcoming exploration of the solar system. As I recall, a trip to Comet 1925 II was ninth on the agenda, after a visit to the Jovian satellite system.* The results will be awaited with interest, especially if a "soft" landing is contemplated.

* Kepler called it the "Jovial" satellite system.

# CHAPTER 20

# Can you remember Halley's comet?

It is my experience that at least half the people you meet over the age of fifty declare positively that they have seen Halley's comet. The last time this famous object was visible was in 1910. To remember this event one must surely have attained the age of three, which means that by 1967 an age of sixty is the very minimum we can allow. If we are to credit the enthusiastic testimony of some, however, they must have been mere infants who viewed the comet from their cradle. Still more incredible is the fact that women are often the most insistent when it comes to the authenticity of their claims.

A typical boyhood recollection goes something like this:

"I was out in the barn milking old Bessie. It was still dark, for we started work pretty early in those days. Well,

I was milking away when my brother yelled from over in the pigpen, 'Hank, come out here and see the comet!' So I run outdoors and there was Halley's comet, just coming up over some sycamores. Grandest sight I'd ever seen. Never forget it if I live to be a hundred. A lot of folks was scared and said it meant the end of the world. But I remembered what Ma told me: 'The comet is a part of God's creation just like the corn and the livestock.' Yes, I'd like to see Halley's comet the next time around. Of course, I'll be eighty next month . . . but I still feel pretty good."

Many people have written me that the sight of Halley's comet was impressed upon them as a child by the unfamiliar experience of being awakened in the darkness of early morning. Still half asleep, their parents took them to the window to see the visitor from outer space. What an awesome sight it was: a huge, ghostly form gleaming in the predawn sky. For weeks they had been listening to stories about the comet: that it foretold the end of the world, that everything was going to be destroyed, and that the Day of Judgement was at hand. Some say they went back to bed convinced that it *did* mean the end of the world. And awakening later in bright sunshine, maybe they felt a little disappointed when they found that everything was still . . . just the same.

WHEN WILL THE COMET RETURN?

According to the orbit of Halley's comet computed at its last return, the period of the comet is 76.03 years. (Fig. 58) Since its last return was in 1910, this means its next visit will be in 1986. Unfortunately, prediction is not that sim-

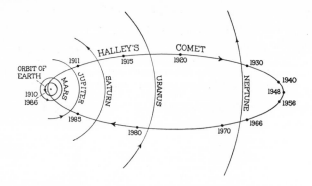

**FIGURE 58.** Position of Halley's comet from its last return in 1910 until its next return in 1986. Notice that the motion of Halley's comet is *retrograde,* or in the opposite direction from the planets in their orbits.

ple. What astronomers try to do is fix the time of perihelion passage as accurately as possible. This means taking into account the disturbing effects of all the planets upon its motion, especially Jupiter and Saturn. These computations are of a very laborious character, and have put a severe burden upon those hardy enough to attempt them. At the next return, this burden can be shifted onto the electronic computer. Apparently no one has had the fortitude to tackle this problem in a serious way, as yet. The only computations I have seen on Halley's comet have all been going backward instead of forward. M. H. Vilyev, a Russian scientist, has recently extended the perturbations of Jupiter and Saturn on Halley's comet from A.D. 451 to 622 B.C. The earliest perihelion passage accurately determined by him is 622.04 B.C. The earliest observed return of Halley's comet on record was probably 240 B.C., but the return due about 163 B.C. has had no certain verification.

M. Kamienski of Poland finds the average interval between returns to be 76.903 years, but the interval has been as short as 74.5 years and as long as 79.3 years. So you might see Halley's comet as early as 1984. Then again, it might be as late as 1989.

## HOW HALLEY'S COMET WAS NAMED

About 1680 Edmund Halley, who later became the Astronomer Royal of England, began an investigation of comets whose repercussions are still felt today. While this work was in progress a bright comet appeared, in 1682, whose orbit Halley determined from the precepts laid down a few years before by Isaac Newton. The elements for the comet of 1682 agreed so closely with those of comets that had appeared in 1607, 1531, and 1456 that Halley became convinced they were not four different comets, but four different returns of the *same* comet. He also suspected that this was the same comet seen in 1378 and 1301. Although the intervals between apparitions varied by a year or two, Halley realized this could be attributed to the perturbations of Jupiter and Saturn. (Uranus and Neptune were as yet unknown.)

Halley delayed until 1705 before venturing to predict when the comet would next return. He set the time for late in 1758, but cautioned that any forecast was necessarily highly uncertain. This seems like hedging on Halley's part, but we must remember that foretelling the return of a comet was a bold prediction in the early eighteenth century. The law of gravitation itself was still a new concept that did not as yet rest upon a firm foundation in fact. Such a prediction was especially rash when applied to a *comet,* one of those erratic objects that darted around the heavens without rhyme or reason. Why, scarcely a century earlier comets were not even supposed to inhabit the realm of the planets, but were looked upon as some sort of sinister exhalations in the upper atmosphere.

It was not surprising, therefore, that Halley's prediction was received with considerable skepticism in some quarters. As his detractors were careful to point out, inasmuch as Halley was then forty-nine, he would have to reach the age of a hundred and two to be on hand to see if his prediction was fulfilled. Was it possible that the great Edmund Halley was seeking publicity for himself in the hope of securing the appointment as Astronomer Royal?

Halley did not fall so far short of the mark at that, not dying until 1742 at the age of eighty-six. As the year 1758 drew near, interest in the comet's reappearance mounted rapidly. Considerable advances had been made in the mathematical methods for computing the motion of a disturbed body, so that Halley's original estimate of the time of perihelion passage could be refigured with much more assurance. A close agreement between theory and observation would be a triumph for the principles of gravitation stated by Newton. It was like a challenge to the mathematical men. And the great French mathematician Alexis Claude Clairaut chose to accept that challenge.

Clairaut should have gotten this ambitious idea much earlier, for the comet was almost upon him before he got to rolling. It was not a simple matter of putting numbers into formulae already known and torture-tested. Thus, his first job was to devise a practical method for computing the perturbations of Saturn and Jupiter. A problem may be solved in theory but the solution is of scant use to the world unless it can be applied in fact. Then after Clairaut had found such a method, he was confronted by still another formidable problem: he had to find somebody who knew how to compute! In this respect he was rather lucky. He found one expert in the noted astronomer Joseph Lalande. The other was not an astronomer or any kind of a scientist at all, but a *woman!* Her name was Mme. Jean André Lepaute, wife of the clockmaker to Louis XVI, who had assisted Lalande in a book on clockmaking by calculating a table giving the number of oscillations per hour for pendulums of different length. So when Clairaut began looking around for a computer to help him on his comet project, she was a natural choice for the job. Later Clairaut remarked that her enthusiasm was boundless, and called her "La savante calculatrice," high praise from one of the foremost mathematicians of the day. Lalande tells us that "although she was not pretty, she did have an elegant figure and a pretty little foot." (!)

For six months the three computed from morning till night, often even at meals, driven by the thought of the comet coming closer . . . closer . . . closer. They had no help from calculating machines, although logarithms must have been available to them. Lalande said that he worked so hard he contracted an ailment which affected him for the rest of his life. Since he was then only twenty-five, and lived until 1807, this meant that he suffered for Halley's comet for half a century. Mme. Lepaute, who was thirty-four, apparently came through the ordeal unscathed, as she continued to be active in astronomy. The last seven years of her life were devoted to caring for her husband, who became ill, crippled, and shut off from all society. She died of typhus in 1788 at the age of sixty-five, a few months before her husband.

On November 14, 1758, Clairaut announced the time of perihelion passage to the Academy of Sciences: April 13, 1759. Although the comet had not been sighted as yet, everyone in Europe who had a telescope was on the watch for it. The prize fell to a farmer near Dresden, who sighted the comet on December 25, 1758. (What a dedicated individual he must have been to be out in the cold on the night of Christmas Day looking for a comet!) It passed perihelion on March 12, 1759, about a month before the time set by Clairaut. This may seem like a wide miss, but when we consider the poor data he had to work with, the agreement is really very good. Edmund Halley was now lauded for his bold prediction, and the comet ever afterward known as *Halley's comet*.

At its next return, in 1835, the comet passed perihelion within five days of the time predicted. With the approach of the comet in 1910 astronomers strove for even greater accuracy. To spur them on, a grand prize of 1000 marks—about $238—was offered for the best paper on the forthcoming return of the famous object. The award went to P. H. Cowell and A. C. D. Crommelin of the Royal Greenwich Observatory. Starting with the perihelion passage of November 16, 1835, they traced the comet's position backward to 1759 and forward to 1910, taking into account the combined attractions of all the planets except Mercury. (Pluto was not discovered until twenty years later.) They were said to have blocked out the path of the comet with such precision that its location was fixed almost to within a matter of yards! Yet Halley's comet passed perihelion 2.7 days behind schedule. The discrepancy seemed incomprehensible at the time but is not regarded so seriously today. Errors undoubtedly were introduced owing to inaccuracies in the values Cowell and Crommelin used for the positions and masses of the planets. Also, the observations on the comet in 1835 were of poor quality, judged by present-day standards.

When will we know the exact date of the next perihelion passage?

Since we can't do anything to hurry the comet on its way, there would seem to be no urgent necessity for launching a crash program twenty years beforehand. In the next twenty years there are sure to be important advances in the technique of making such calculations. So why not wait until we can take advantage of them?

HALLEY'S COMET LOOKS AT THE
WORLD OF 1910

Looking backward from half a century, we find it hard to understand how the newspapers in 1910 managed to fill the front page. (Fig. 59) Compared with our times, there wasn't any news. William Howard Taft, who had taken office a year earlier, was proving somewhat of a disappointment as chief executive. The burning issues of the day were Votes for Women, the tariff, and trust busting. The lives of the people back there seem so secure and tranquil. Yet they didn't consider it so; in fact, they

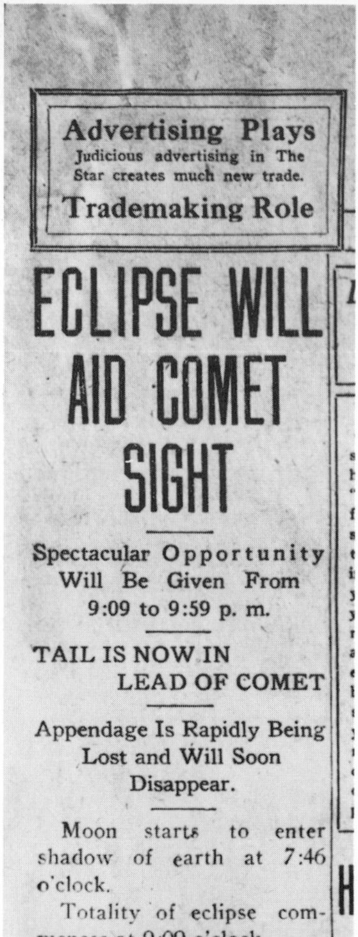

Advertising Plays
Judicious advertising in The Star creates much new trade.
Trademaking Role

ECLIPSE WILL AID COMET SIGHT

Spectacular Opportunity Will Be Given From 9:09 to 9:59 p. m.

TAIL IS NOW IN LEAD OF COMET

Appendage Is Rapidly Being Lost and Will Soon Disappear.

Moon starts to enter shadow of earth at 7:46 o'clock.

Totality of eclipse commences at 9:09 o'clock.

Totality of eclipse ends at 9:59 o'clock.

Moon emerges from shadow at 11:22 o'clock.

Halley's comet, tail and all, will make its most spectacular appearance tonight in the western sky, when it will reign comparatively alone in celestial glory for three hours and a half, and will be for fifty minutes a brilliant luminary while the moon is totally eclipsed by the earth.

According to Dr. George Ellery Hale, director of the Carnegie solar observatory at Mount Wilson, the moon's eclipse will begin at 7:46 o'clock tonight. The total phase of the eclipse will commence at 9:09 and end at 9:59 o'clock. The moon will be out of the shadow at 11:22 o'clock. With the light of the moon out of the sky, the comet with its tail or tails will become visible in all its brilliancy, and the scientific observations

FIGURE 59. Front page of Pasadena *Star*, May 23, 1910, with story of lunar eclipse when Halley's comet was also visible.

thought they were living it up pretty fast. Read their poetry:

"I am tired of the showy seeming,
  Of a life that is half a lie,
  Of the faces lined with scheming,
  In the throng that hurries by." *

From Cowell and Crommelin's work, astronomers knew pretty accurately where the comet should appear in the constellation of Gemini. Observatories were naturally eager to be the first to sight the comet. In the summer of 1909 telescopes were already being trained in the direction of The Twins.

While the world was straining to catch the first glimpse of Halley's comet, a wholly unexpected object flashed into view. It was discovered by so many people that it has always been known simply by its official designation of 1910 I. This glamorous newcomer became bright enough to be easily visible in full daylight. Yet it attracted little public attention, probably because people didn't know where to look for it by day; and when in the night sky was rather faint. 1910 I was moving in a parabolic orbit and will never be seen again.

Halley's comet was first identified on photographs taken by Max Wolf at Heidelberg on September 11, 1909, when 300 million miles from the sun. Once the comet was found and its motion accurately determined from observation, astronomers could backtrack hoping that someone had photographed it accidentally without realizing the fact. Such a search revealed that the Helwan Observatory in Egypt had picked it up on a plate taken three weeks

* John Boyle O'Reilly (1844–1890).

earlier. At this stage Halley's comet looked no different from the faint stars around it, and could only be identified by its motion from night to night.

The comet at discovery was a morning object, rising about five hours before the sun. By early December it was opposite the sun, and therefore rose when the sun was setting. Late in March of 1910 it was back again in the morning sky, where it remained until it transited the sun on May 18, to become an evening object. (Fig. 60)

It is this apparently erratic motion that has given comets their bad reputation. Of course, their motion is no more "erratic" than that of the planets. Even among scientific men the feeling still lingers that comets cheat on the law of gravitation a little. As Elizabeth Roemer,* an authority on comets and their orbits, has said, "The impression has become increasingly widespread that comets are affected by large forces, unpredictable in nature, that cause large deviations from the motion predicted by gravitational forces alone. That impression is plainly unjustified. What deviations there are, if indeed there are any measurable ones, are extremely small." Time and again astronomers have suspected the law of gravitation was at fault, only to find the trouble was due to inaccuracies in their theories and observations.

Halley's comet was closest to the earth on May 20, when its distance was 14.3 million miles, and its velocity relative to the earth 52 miles per second. Its exceptionally rapid motion is due to the fact that Halley's is a retrograde comet; that is, a comet that revolves in the opposite direction to the earth in its orbit. On May 21 we probably

* U.S. Naval Observatory, Flagstaff Station, Arizona.

FIGURE 60.  Halley's comet photographed on May 29, 1910, by Seth B. Nicholson. Nicholson took this photograph with an 8¼-inch telescope while a student at Drake University, Des Moines, Iowa. Later, as a professional astronomer, he discovered four of the satellites of Jupiter.

passed through the comet's tail. Although the prophets of doom were loud in their wail, nobody seemed any the worse for the experience. (Fig. 61)

As if having a bright comet in the sky were not bad enough, there was also an eclipse of the moon on May 23, 1910. This was another portent of evil, apparently sent along to aid and abet the machinations of the comet.

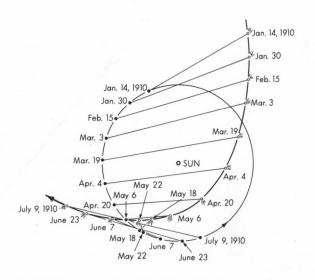

FIGURE 61.   The positions of earth and Halley's comet during interval of closest approach. The comet passed nearest earth on May 20, 1910, when its distance was 14,300,000 miles. Since comet and earth were moving in nearly opposite directions, they passed with the high velocity of 52 miles per second. The earth probably passed through the tail of Halley's comet on May 21. (Courtesy of Griffith Observatory, Los Angeles, California.)

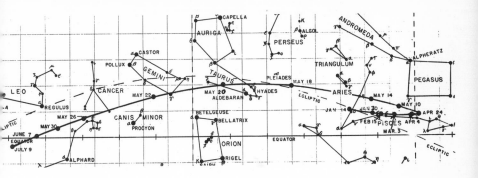

F I G U R E  62.   Path of Halley's comet relative to stars at time
of transit of sun of May 18, 1910.

Halley's comet began to slow down, until by July it was
practically motionless among the stars of Leo, and by the
end of June had faded beyond the reach of the eye. But
astronomers were able to follow it photographically until
June 1911, when it was 520 million miles from the sun, a
little beyond the orbit of Jupiter. (Fig. 62)

The return of Halley's comet in 1910 was unique in
being the only one in the last 2000 years when the earth
was at peace (aside from a little war in Egypt and a revolution in Nicaragua). Imagine the comet to be a living
organism endowed with superhuman powers of perception. What a discouraging sight the earth must be! It comes
by every three-quarters of a century. And every time it
finds the earth convulsed in bloodshed and violence.

"Earth is the most favored planet in the solar system,"
it reflects, "a planet neither too hot nor too cold, blessed
with an abundance of oxygen, and water, and a fine big
satellite to keep it company. What a wonderful world
earth could be . . . if only it weren't for the people!"

# CHAPTER 21

## *The origin of comets*

I have often thought that the craters on the moon were put there chiefly for the purpose of keeping people on the earth busy conjuring up theories of their origin. This era of happy speculation will soon be a thing of the past, crushed under the advancing march of technology. But opportunities still abound. Take comets, for instance: What are they? How did they get here? Where did they come from?

Of the several hypotheses of the origin of comets that have been proposed, only two will be considered here. Both are about a century and a half old, and should be accorded a certain degree of respect for their age and durability if nothing else. Both have recently been upgraded with modern improvements. First we shall discuss the comet-cloud hypothesis, developed with considerable success beginning about 1950 by J. H. Oort of the University Observatory, Leiden. The second is the new ejec-

tion hypothesis advanced in 1953 by S. K. Vsekhsviatskii
of the Astronomical Observatory, Kiev, U.S.S.R.

Not until the appearance of the bright comet of 1577
did we have any scientific knowledge of the distance of
comets. Tycho Brahe, the great Danish astronomer, by
comparing positions of this comet relative to the stars
when viewed from several widely separated stations, demonstrated that it must be at least as far away as the moon.
(Previously it had been supposed they originated in the
upper atmosphere.) This immediately raised new questions: Are comets members of the solar system? Or do
they come from the region of the stars?

Fortunately we have a criterion capable of giving us
a definite answer. We saw in the chapter on comet orbits
that a body moving under the gravitational attraction of
the sun must revolve in an ellipse, parabola, or hyperbola.
The planets revolve in ellipses of such low eccentricity as
to be scarcely distinguishable from circles. With a few exceptions, comets revolve in extremely elongated ellipses,
many of which for simplicity are regarded as parabolic.
The parabola is an open curve with an eccentricity of 1.
It is thus a special type of curve, like the circle. If the
eccentricity exceeds 1, the curve is a hyperbola. Obviously,
a real body moves in either an ellipse or hyperbola. Even
if a body were started moving in a circle or parabola, the
disturbing attraction of the other members of the solar
system would immediately change the orbit to an ellipse
or hyperbola. Now the *permanent* members of the solar
system *must* move in ellipses (closed curves), or we would
not continue to see them regularly. Like a parabola, a
hyperbola is an open curve. An object moving along a hyperbolic path would visit the solar system but once, then

leave for good. The nature of a comet's orbit gives us just the criterion we need to ascertain its origin. Did the comet come from the region of the stars? If the orbit is elliptical—no. If hyperbolic—yes.

The trouble is that we can only observe comets over such an extremely limited portion of their path. Suppose a comet is moving in an immensely long ellipse with a period of 4 million years. We are able to observe it for four months. From these observations we compute the elements of its orbit. The orbit comes out hyperbolic, with an eccentricity of $e = 1.0005$. So the comet came from the stars. But did it? How much faith can we put in the accuracy of these elements? We can represent the observations just as well by a parabola or a near-parabolic ellipse. All we know is that wherever the comet came from, it was a long ways from here.

Of some 2000 comets in recorded history, about 800 have had their orbits computed. Many of these were successive returns of the same comet: Halley's comet has been observed at twenty-nine apparitions and Encke's comet at forty-seven. Among comets which have been exceptionally well observed, there are about fifty with orbits that are slightly hyperbolic, the one with highest eccentricity being 1886 III, for which $e = 1.0130$. What can we say about the origin of these fifty objects?

Consider a comet still far beyond Pluto approaching the sun in a near-parabolic ellipse. The comet may enter the solar system and leave it in practically the same orbit as it came. Should it make a close approach to one of the major planets, however, its orbit may be drastically changed. Jupiter, owing to its great mass, is by far the most effective in this respect. The nature of the change

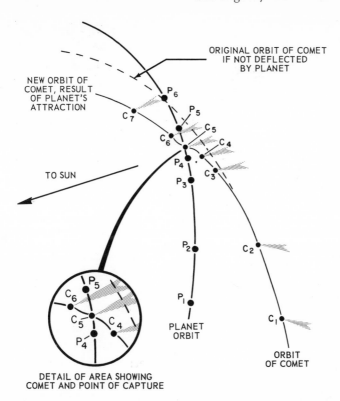

ORIGINAL ORBIT OF COMET
IF NOT DEFLECTED
BY PLANET

NEW ORBIT OF
COMET, RESULT
OF PLANET'S
ATTRACTION

TO SUN

DETAIL OF AREA SHOWING
COMET AND POINT OF CAPTURE

PLANET
ORBIT

ORBIT
OF COMET

FIGURE 63. Illustrating change in path of comet due to close encounter with a planet. (Ray Benton, Melpar, Inc. Drawing by George D. Schwald.)

will depend upon how the encounter occurs. A comet with a period of a million years may find itself changed into a member of Jupiter's family with a period of ten years. Or it may work the other way. A short-period comet after a close brush with Jupiter may be sent heading for the stars in a hyperbolic orbit. (Fig. 63)

Thus the fact that we occasionally find a comet moving

in a hyperbolic orbit does not necessarily signify it to be an interstellar object, a genuine "outsider." Originally, the comet's orbit may have been an ellipse, and it may not have become hyperbolic until *after* entering the solar system. To find out, we have to run the comet backward over its path a step at a time, including in each step the attraction of the planets, until we have it far outside the solar system where their perturbations may be neglected. Only then will we know the true character of its orbit.

Results are available for twenty comets which had been sufficiently well observed to make such an elaborate analysis meaningful. Not a single one was originally hyperbolic. It is hard to resist the conclusion that ALL comets move in ellipses and that ALL are members of the solar system. But what a solar system! No longer is it a little discus-shaped area around the sun enclosed by the orbit of Pluto. Instead, the solar system expands until it fills a volume of space reaching almost to the stars.

## THE COMET-CLOUD HYPOTHESIS

The starting point for the comet-cloud hypothesis is the peculiar distribution in the aphelia of the long-period comets. (It will be recalled that aphelion is the point on an orbit farthest from the sun.) In the case of the long-period comets, we can think of their aphelia as "the place where the comets come from." If we went strictly by the rules to find the distance to aphelion, we would have to know both the eccentricity of an orbit and the length of the semimajor axis. But if the orbit is sufficiently elongated, the distance to aphelion is practically identical with the length of the major axis, as is evident from Table 5. It is shown in celestial mechanics that the total energy of an orbit depends only upon the length of the major axis. Suppose we calculate the total energy of some cometary orbits, using values of their major axes *before* entry into the solar system, and list them in order from smallest to largest. We would expect their energies to be spread fairly evenly over a wide range of distances. Instead, comets show a decided preference for certain values more than others. This can hardly be due to chance or the way the material was selected. Apparently it represents a real characteristic of the orbits of long-period comets.

The fact that the aphelia of these comets cluster around certain particular values is highly significant. For if the

T A B L E   5

| Name | Object | Eccentricity | Length of major axis | Aphelion distance |
|---|---|---|---|---|
| Venus | Planet | 0.0068 | 1.446 | 0.728 |
| Mercury | " | .2056 | 0.774 | 0.467 |
| Hidalgo | Asteroid | .65 | 11.42 | 9.422 |
| P/Johnson | Comet | .703 | 7.23 | 4.97 |
| P/Tuttle | " | .821 | 11.40 | 10.38 |
| P/Crommelin | " | .919 | 18.38 | 17.64 |
| P/Pons-Brooks | " | .955 | 34.24 | 33.47 |
| P/Ross | " | .981 | 32.26 | 31.95 |
| P/Mellish | " | 0.993 | 55.3 | 55.1 |

comets had passed through the solar system before, their orbits would have been changed until their aphelia *were* scattered over a wide range of values. Hence these must be NEW COMETS, deserving of our closest attention. For in them we may find the clue that will lead us to their place of origin.

## THE REALM OF THE COMETS

Investigation reveals that the long-period comets occupy the space within a spherical shell surrounding the sun from 30,000 AU to 100,000 AU in thickness. The comet cloud is smeared uniformly throughout this space; that is, they do not favor one direction in space more than another. Comets at such vast distances from the sun move so slowly that practically their entire lifetime is spent in this region. Although the outer boundary of the cloud is at a distance comparable with the nearer stars, yet the comets are bona fide members of the solar system. Table 6 gives the distances of some representative objects, expressed in astronomical units and in light years.

Although true members of the solar system, the long-period comets are not bound to the sun by the same firm ties as the planets. Given a little assistance, it is possible for them to make their escape. Let us see how much additional velocity a comet would need to attain escape velocity at various points in its orbit.

First we will consider the situation of a comet 60,000 AU from the sun at the aphelion of its orbit. It is creeping along at 0.000554 miles per second, or about 2 miles per hour in more familiar terms. The velocity of escape at

# T A B L E   6

| Object | Distance in AUs | Distance in LY |
|---|---|---|
| Sun | 1 | 0.0000158 |
| Pluto | 40 | 0.0006326 |
| Inner radius of comet cloud | 30,000 | 0.4745 |
| Outer radius of comet cloud | 100,000 | 1.58 |
| Proxima  Centauri | 271,000 | 4.3 |
| Sirius | 546,000 | 8.7 |
| Rigel | 52,600,000 | 815 |

60,000 AU is 0.106727 miles per second. Which means that the comet need only increase its velocity by 0.106727 — 0.000554 = 0.106173 miles per second to get loose from the solar system forever. This would seem to be the easiest place for a comet to effect an escape, when it is far from the sun and its attraction correspondingly reduced.

After several million years in this zone, the comet is now approaching the perihelion of its orbit. To be specific, it is 5.2 AU from the sun, about to cross the orbit of Jupiter. Its velocity has increased from practically nothing to 11.46347 miles per second. What is the velocity of escape at 5.2 AU? It is 11.46397 miles per second. Which means that the comet needs only 0.00050 miles per second more to take off for infinity! How easy it would be for Jupiter to effect the transition from ellipse to hyperbola!

Whatever changes Jupiter makes will occur very quickly, in a matter of days or hours, if the encounter be a very close one.

A comet would therefore seem very safe and secure cruising near the aphelion of its orbit with nothing to disturb it but the stars hundreds of thousands of astronomical units away. No need to worry about *them*, you might think. It is true that their attraction is extremely feeble. *But it acts for millions of years.* And it builds and builds. . . .

Statistical studies show that of the new comets entering the solar system about half will leave the sun in hyperbolic orbits, the other half being thrown into elliptic orbits with aphelia of about 10,000 AU and periods of 400,000 years. At this rate of extinction, one would think that all the comets capable of coming near the sun would have taken their *congé* long ago. Yet there still seems to be no lack of comets in the solar system.

It is here that the stars come to our aid. If the cloud were undisturbed, it is possible that a rather acute situation might eventually develop in terrestrially directed comets. But stellar perturbations keep the cloud in a state of turbulence, continually throwing comets into new orbits that will take them near the sun. The depletion process proceeds so slowly that there is still an abundant supply of comets in the comet "icebox." How do we keep comets coming our way? This part of the theory is almost too easy. To keep comets coming our way it is only necessary to assume enough comets.

One minor point remains to be mentioned. How did the comet cloud get there in the first place?

The process generally envisioned is one of "comets by

catastrophe." There once was a planet revolving between Mars and Jupiter. For reasons unknown it exploded, its shattered fragments flying in all directions. Those that went into orbits of low eccentricity remained in the solar system. Solar radiation soon reduced them to the bare rocks we call the asteroids. Others were diffused into hyperbolic orbits by the planets and were lost. Many were thrown into elongated ellipses that took them far from the sun. These particles retained their gaseous constituents and now form the comet cloud. A planet as massive as the earth would have supplied ample material for the comets, asteroids, and meteoroids together.

## THE NEW EJECTION HYPOTHESIS

Toward the close of the eighteenth century, when that great mathematician the Marquis de Laplace was dallying with the nebular hypothesis and comets from interstellar space, another famous French mathematician, Joseph Louis Lagrange, suggested that comets might originate by ejection from the planets. Nearly a century later the same mechanism was evoked by R. A. Proctor and others in an attempt to explain why so many of the short-period comets have their aphelia at about the distance (Fig. 64) of Jupiter. The explanation was simplicity itself: their aphelia were situated near Jupiter because they came from Jupiter, born from the surface of Jove by volcanic ejection. Such a hypothesis seemed much more plausible half a century ago than today. Formerly Jupiter was regarded as a "sort of semi-sun—hot, though not so hot as to be self-luminous." This image of Jupiter lingered on into the 1920s, when

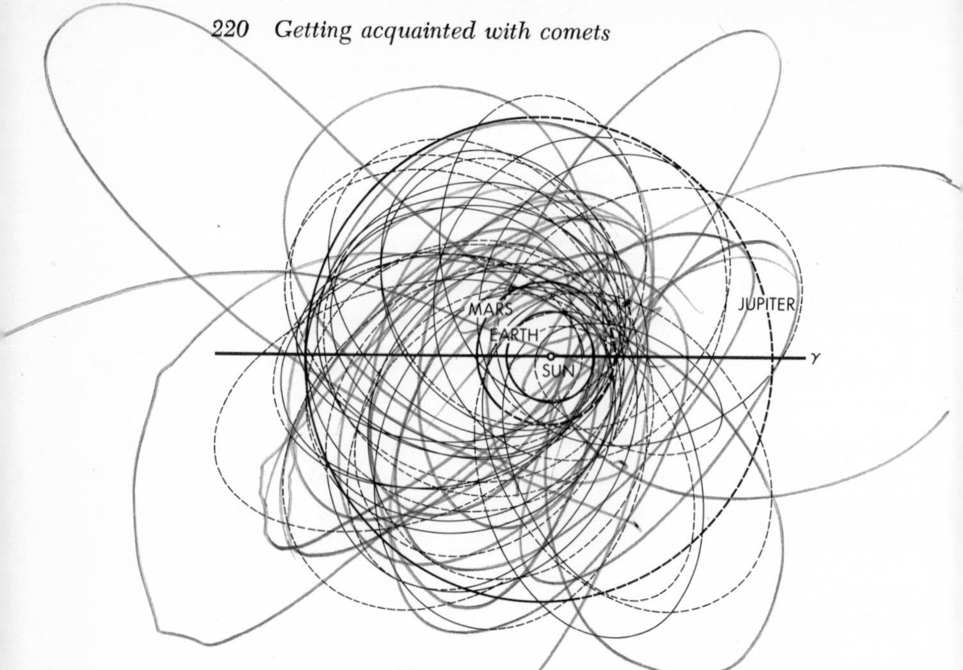

FIGURE 64. The large number of short-period comets with aphelia near the orbit of Jupiter are considered members of Jupiter's "family."

measures with the thermocouple showed its surface temperature was below that of dry ice. But conditions below the atmosphere were still a matter of conjecture. Strong and continued volcanic activity appears to be the most likely explanation for the violent changes observed in the cloud belts. The unexpected discovery of radio emission from Jupiter in 1955 indicates the presence of powerful sources of energy on the planet.

Recently, attention has been directed again to the Jovian ejection hypothesis by S. K. Vsekhsviatskii and his associates. They point out that the known number of comets in the Jupiter family is far larger than the planet could have acquired by capture, about 100,000 times larger, in their estimation. They find the lifetime of the short-period comets to be so brief that Jupiter could not conceivably acquire replacements as fast as the old members of his family wear out.

They also consider it highly significant that several members of the family, when their motion is projected backward, are found to have been very close to Jupiter *prior* to discovery. Notable examples are comets Lexell, Brorsen, Wolf I, Brooks II, Giacobini-Zinner, and Oterma, all of which have passed through Jupiter's satellite system. So far as is known, the record for a close approach is held by P/Brooks II, discovered in 1889, which on July 20, 1886, passed within 55,000 miles of the planet's surface. Vsekhsviatskii asserts that such cases speak directly in favor of the ejection of comets "before the very eyes of the observer."

When we examine the Jovian ejection hypothesis more closely, however, we find grave difficulties in the way. A comet, to be born of Jove, must first get free of its surface. The velocity of escape for Jupiter is 37 miles per second, about five times that for the earth. This is the escape velocity as calculated from the observed equatorial diameter of the planet, which includes the atmosphere. The escape velocity from the solid surface will be higher, how much higher depending upon the depth of the atmosphere. In the last thirty years various authorities have estimated the depth of the atmosphere as somewhere between 100 miles and 10,000 miles. If we assume the worst and make it 10,000 miles, the escape velocity at the solid surface would then be 42 miles per second.

Even if energy sources exist within Jupiter capable of

imparting such a velocity to a body, that alone is not necessarily going to make a comet out of it. To be made into a comet, the body must first penetrate the atmosphere and *then* have enough velocity left to achieve escape. We accomplish this feat on the earth by keeping a rocket in powered flight until through the bulk of the atmosphere at about 40 miles, after which it can safely be accelerated to escape velocity. But does a volcano have the technical know-how to launch a comet successfully? A volcano would give a body an initial powerful impulse, after which it is strictly on its own. A. Corlin has estimated that a particle on the surface of Jupiter would need an initial velocity of 370 miles per second to get through the atmosphere and escape. Considerations such as these pose such formidable problems that the proponents of the Jovian ejection hypothesis have been forced to abandon it as unrealistic.

Yet the fact remains that the aphelia of the short-period comets still cluster around the orbit of Jupiter. There must be a tie-in somewhere . . . Eureka! If not Jupiter, why not the moons of Jupiter? They ought to be good for something.

This is exactly what Vsekhsviatskii has done. He has transferred the source of comets from Jupiter to its four big satellites, Io, Europa, Ganymede, and Callisto. And what a difference it makes! No need now to worry about an impossibly high escape velocity. No atmosphere to penetrate. And we can still account for Jupiter's comet family!

As already noted, one of the strong arguments urged in favor of the ejection hypothesis is the brief lifespan of the short-period comets. According to Vsekhsviatskii, in 225 years Jupiter has lost 27 comets out of an original family of 68. At this rate of extinction, if we made Jupiter a present of 1000 comets, and no more were available to him, they would fade away somewhat as follows:

T A B L E   7

| Time (years) | Number of comets |
|---|---|
| 0 | 1000 |
| 10 | 978 |
| 100 | 799 |
| 500 | 325 |
| 1000 | 106 |
| 2000 | 11 |

After 3000 years Jupiter would be down to 1.18 comets. Now 3000 years is only a moment in cosmic history. If short-period comets wear out as fast as Vsekhsviatskii believes, their continued presence in the solar system is very puzzling indeed.

But are they fading so fast? Everyone does not agree. N. T. Bobrovnikoff, from his investigation of P/Wolf I, thinks otherwise. This faint comet discovered in 1883 has probably been the object of more study than any other comet known, with the exception of Encke's. According to Vsekhsviatskii, P/Wolf I has been fading by 0.5 to 1.0 magnitude at every revolution, and now is barely on the limit of telescopic observation. Bobrovnikoff, on the other hand, from an intercomparison of the brightness of P/Wolf I at its six returns from 1884 to 1925, was unable to find definite evidence for any fading whatever. He points out, too, that if this comet is fading as we go forward in time, then it should be brightening as we go backward in time. At the rate of fading that Vsekhsviatskii claims for it, P/Wolf I would have been a naked-eye object in 1800, and could hardly have escaped detection until eighty-three years later. To which the ejection-hypothesis people retort that calculations show P/Wolf I to have been within the Jovian satellite system on June 8, 1875. No wonder it wasn't discovered earlier. It hadn't been born yet!

Vsekhsviatskii is convinced that volcanism has been and probably still is an important factor in planetary evolution that has never received the attention it deserves. He cites in evidence the bright flares observed on Mars by T. Saheki; the great abundance of carbon dioxide and yellowish dust in the atmosphere of Venus; and the white outbursts occasionally observed on Saturn. The existence of craters on Mars, revealed by the Mariner IV pictures, might seem to support the volcanic hypothesis, but it is more likely they originated by meteoritic impact rather than volcanic action.

What the ejection-hypothesis people should do is to keep a continuous patrol on the four big Jovian satellites. It would certainly help if they could catch a comet in the actual process of *accouchement* from one of the moons. The prospect of making such an observation must be slightly better than holding a winning ticket on the Irish Sweepstakes three times in a row.

# CHAPTER 22

# Cometary exploration: the future

The ideal way to improve our knowledge of comets would be by an on-the-spot investigation. Man-on-a-comet has been done many times in imagination. About a century ago, in *Hector Servedoff*, Jules Verne had a comet side-swipe the earth, taking a French soldier into space along with it. Mark Twain used the same device in *Captain Stormfield's Visit to Heaven*. But of course these were nothing but *fantasy*. Within a decade or so, however, the same idea may work out in *fact*.

In the study of the heavenly bodies, knowledge is not necessarily related to proximity. Venus comes closer than any other major member of the solar system except the moon, yet how meager is our knowledge of this body. (Come to think of it, how much do we know for sure about the moon?) Many comets have come closer than Venus, which approaches to within 26 million miles every 584 days. But as we have seen, we still are unable to answer some of the most obvious questions about comets. What is the source of their luminosity? Why do their tails point away from the sun? What is the relationship between comets and meteor showers? Why are some comets so durable and others so prone to disruption? And a dozen others. One trouble, of course, is that most comets are so faint that it is difficult or impossible to study them spectroscopically. Also, in the case of an object like a comet that shows us a disk, coming closer doesn't make its surface appear any brighter. And bright comets are so rare that a systematic observing program is impossible. In general, comets have been such unrewarding objects for study that until recently astrophysicists have paid them scant attention. But now we are entering a new era of exploration within the solar system. The spectacular results of the Ranger moon shots, the Mariner II examination of Venus, and particularly the incredibly successful Mariner IV mission to Mars have given the comet men new hope: hope that they can soon secure the information on comets they have been wanting so long—not by make-do, indirect methods, but at first hand from the source itself.

To make contact (or very close contact) with an object revolving around the sun, we must be able to determine its position very accurately at any time in the future. This we can do for the moon, Venus, and Mars. We have had accurate observations of these bodies beginning with Tycho Brahe some 350 years ago. The principal business of the U.S. Naval Observatory at Washington, D.C., is keeping track of the sun, moon, and planets. The precision of which we are capable now was demonstrated in the most striking way when Mariner IV was sent across 335 million miles of space to within 200 miles of its rendezvous position with Mars.

The situation is more difficult when it comes to intercepting a comet. Comets are only observable at intervals of several years, and then only over the portion of their orbit near perihelion. For a successful comet-intercept experiment, we must not miss the nucleus by more than 100,000 miles. That sounds like quite a liberal margin for error, but actually it is doubtful if we could attain that degree of accuracy in the case of a bright new unexpected comet.

Why not use a bright periodic comet like Halley's? We have observations on Halley's comet at every one of its twenty-seven returns from 87 B.C. to A.D. 1910. But the seventy-six-year period of Halley's comet rules it out immediately. If we missed it the first shot, we would have to wait another three-quarters of a century for the second try! Besides, Halley's comet won't be near again till 1986, and that's too long to wait.

Practical considerations, therefore, limit us to comets having well-determined orbits with periods not exceeding ten years. Only about thirty such objects are known. Out of these, only one meets all the requirements—Encke's. Encke's comet has a period of 3.3 years, the shortest of any comet known.* It has been observed at practically every one of its perihelion passages since it was discovered (or rediscovered) by Pons in 1818. No comet has had so much intensive work done on its orbit by so many first-class men as Encke's.

---

* Comet Wilson-Harrington has a period of 2.3 years but was only seen once, in 1949.

POSSIBILITIES OF A COMET-INTERCEPT
EXPERIMENT*

Comet-intercept experiments are of two types:

1. Experiments that could be carried out immediately
with instruments and methods already known.

2. Experiments that might be carried out sometime in
the future based upon the experience gained with present
probes and the advances in technology acquired from
them.

We have told how the American Astronomical Society
in 1910 sent an astronomer 2200 miles across the ocean
from Pasadena to Honolulu to observe Halley's comet.
Now we are planning another expedition for the purpose
of observing a comet. This time the plans call for sending
a probe 150 million miles across space to the comet itself.
We estimated the budget expedition of 1910 at $2000. No
figures are available for the comet-intercept experiment,
but it will probably be considerably higher.

The main objective is the same as that of the mission to
Honolulu in 1910: to gain information on the nature of the
nucleus. This could be done by TV photography of the
nucleus at close range. Besides settling the question of the
size and mass of the nucleus, it should tell us whether it
conforms to the sand-bank model or the icy-conglomerate
model (or some other model that nobody has thought of
yet). Let us not forget that the Russian photos of the
moon's far side didn't look at all the way we confidently
expected. We expected the far side would show great dark

* Most of this material has been abstracted from *Comet Intercept
Study* by Space Technology Laboratories, Inc., Redondo Beach,
California.

FIGURE 65. Artist's conception of a future rocket probe through a natural comet. (Illustration by George D. Schwald for *Exploring the Comets* by Ray Benton, Melpar, Inc.)

plains, the same as the moon's near side. On the contrary, large dark areas are rare on the far side—which didn't fit in with our theories of the evolution of the lunar surface at all. If we were so badly mistaken about the moon—the *nearest* body in space—think how wrong we could be about a comet! (Fig. 65)

We have emphasized that except for some slight curvature due to a comet's motion, its tail points in the opposite direction from the sun. So far no one has been able to devise a completely satisfactory theory to account for the motion of material away from the sun, either by light pressure or encounters between the tail particles and corpuscles emitted by the sun (the "solar wind"). The effect could be explained by a solar wind, however, if a cometary magnetic field exists. The behavior of filaments and streamers in the head suggest the presence of a magnetic field but cannot be accepted as proof. If independent evidence for a cometary magnetic field could be obtained, the theory would be greatly strengthened. Since magnetometers have already been flown successfully on satellites and space probes, the inclusion of a magnetometer on a comet probe should present no difficulties.

Information on the particles that produce the solar-reflection spectrum in comets could be obtained from detectors that would move through the coma and record impacts received from cometary material. Detectors have been developed capable of measuring the electrical charge, intensity of impact, and the number of impacts per second. The size and shape of the particles will influence the appearance of the continuous-background spectrum of the comet, and this would appear to be the easiest way to learn about them. It has always been difficult to secure suitable cometary spectra, so that conclusions drawn from them regarding the nature of the particles are correspondingly uncertain.

Valuable information on the chemical composition of comets could be obtained from large-scale photographs of their spectra. But getting closer to a comet would be of little advantage here. It seems contrary to reason that a photograph of the spectrum of the coma taken at half a million miles would not be an improvement over one taken at 5 million miles. But the fact is that as long as a body presents a surface to us, its brightness *per unit area* remains unchanged, regardless of its distance. This is illustrated in a striking way by photographs of the planets. If an exposure time of 5 seconds is right for Mars at 80 million miles, it is still right for Mars at 40 million miles. The planet looms much brighter in the sky. But the disk is no brighter than before. Similarly, moving in for a close shot on a comet would be of no help so far as brightness of image is concerned. With a probe we could photograph the spectrum of the comet in the ultraviolet, which is blotted out by the atmosphere for observatories on earth. But if ultraviolet photography is all we want, there is no need to send a camera millions of miles to the comet. We could do ultraviolet photography just as well from an orbiting satellite.

## THE CHRONOLOGY OF A COMET

P/Encke has achieved so much status as the only comet suitable for an intercept experiment that a few words about its history may be of interest.

It is hard to say when Encke's comet was discovered. Although first observed by Méchain in 1786, it had to be discovered three more times before its identity was finally recognized. On November 26, 1818, Jean Louis Pons at Marseilles sighted a telescopic comet which he followed for the next seven weeks. The object aroused the interest of Johann Franz Encke, a German mathematical astronomer then twenty-seven years of age. The astronomers of those days supposed that comets all moved in nearly para-

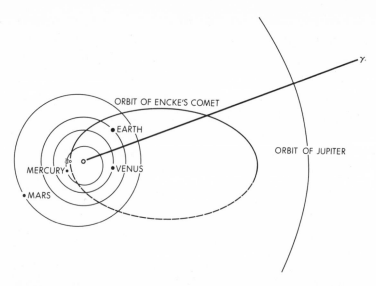

FIGURE 66. Position of planets at perihelion passage of Encke's comet, Oct. 20, 1957.

bolic orbits, but it soon became apparent to Encke that this one was moving in an elliptical orbit with a period of only about 3.5 years. (Fig. 66) Its orbital elements agreed so closely with comets observed in 1786, 1795, and 1805 that he was almost sure these were different returns of Pons' comet. Being "almost sure," however, is not the same as being *sure* and Encke's curiosity was aroused to such a degree that he could have no rest until the matter was settled. To do this he had to start with the position of the comet in 1818, and trace its motion back to 1786, allowing for the perturbing effects of the planets whenever significant. This was no small job for one man, and must have been extremely laborious without modern computing aids. Yet within only six weeks he had carried the work through

and established conclusively that Pons' comet of 1818 was
identical with the three previously observed; and furthermore, it evidently had passed perihelion seven times between 1786 and 1818 without being detected. This is a
good illustration of how often it is just as important to be
able to deduce what *has happened* as what is *going to
happen.*

Encke predicted the time of the comet's next return in
1822 with such sensational accuracy that astronomers forever afterward have called it "Encke's comet." Encke did
most of this research before his thirtieth year, while still
studying under the great Karl Friedrich Gauss at Göttingen. Somehow he found time to acquire his knowledge
of celestial mechanics from 1811 to 1815 in spite of active
military service as a sergeant-major in the horse artillery.

As early as August 1820, Encke had suspected that the
motion of the comet was gradually accelerating. After
eliminating the disturbing effects of the planets, the times
of perihelion passage from 1786 to 1819 indicated the
period was getting shorter, or the comet was moving
faster, at the rate of 0.11 days per revolution. When the
comet showed a diminution of 0.11 days again in 1822 he
felt justified in announcing that some unknown force must
be acting upon it. He was thus led to his famous hypothesis
of a resisting medium near the sun which, by opposing the
motion of the comet, was increasing its average velocity.

That a body can have its velocity *increased* by something that *resists* its motion is in direct contradiction to
all our everyday experience with moving bodies. But our
experience with automobiles and lawn mowers is not directly comparable to the motion of bodies in space orbiting around the sun.

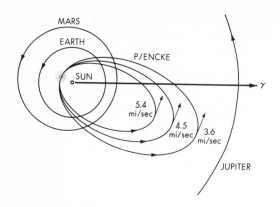

FIGURE 67. Changes that would occur in the orbit of P/Encke if velocity were decreased by 1 per cent at perihelion passage. Result is that orbit shrinks and velocity is increased elsewhere.

Suppose that all the resisting material is located near the perihelion of the comet's orbit, the rest of the orbit being free from friction. (Fig. 67) We will use a hypothetical comet for which the effect of the resistance is vastly exaggerated: during each perihelion passage its velocity is reduced by 1 per cent. Now there is nothing mysterious about it: the dust cloud *does* slow the comet down at perihelion. In doing so, it immediately alters the size and shape of the *whole orbit*. Originally, our comet had a velocity of 43.11 miles per second at perihelion, which was enough to make it recede to 380 million miles from the sun at aphelion. But now, as the result of this slowdown, the aphelion distance is reduced to 316 million miles. In fact, the whole orbit undergoes a shrinking process, at the same time becoming less eccentric.

Now here is where the tricky part comes in. The velocity of a body depends upon its distance from the sun: the *nearer* the sun, the *more* the velocity. Since the comet at aphelion is nearer the sun than before, its velocity at aphelion is also more, increasing from 3.6 miles per second to 4.5 miles per second. In fact, the velocity of the comet is increased all the way around its orbit—*except* in the vicinity of perihelion.

By including an arbitrary correction in his figures for a thin resisting medium near the sun, Encke was able to predict the future returns of his comet very accurately. In 1861 he published a summary of his work, covering all the observations of the comet from 1786 to 1858, including twenty-two returns. At each return the period was shorter by 0.11 days. The comet's behavior was in such close accord with the theory of motion perturbed by a resisting medium that Encke believed there was strong evidence for its existence.

After Encke's death in 1865 at the age of seventy-four, the task of looking after his comet was turned over to von Asten at the Pulkovo Observatory, a grave responsibility for a young man of twenty-five. His troubles began at once. For the comet which had behaved so obediently under Encke's supervision refused to acknowledge the authority of its new master. At its next return in 1868 the acceleration showed a decrease of 50 per cent. And at the return of 1871 it vanished altogether! The comet's motion was so different from before that von Asten decided to make an entirely new investigation of the eighteen observed apparitions from 1819 to 1875. He confirmed Encke's hypothesis of an acceleration produced by a constant resistance at perihelion, and was able to predict its motion satisfactorily except for its sudden disappearance in 1871. The only explanation he could offer was the unlikely hypothesis of a collision with some asteroid. Von Asten's work was cut short by his death in 1878 at the age of thirty-six.

The problem of the motion of Encke's comet was now assumed by Oskar Backlund, also of the Pulkovo Ob-

servatory. He found the whole situation in a most unsatis-
factory condition. In fact, it was in such a confused state
that he decided—as von Asten had done—to start all over
again from 1819!

Backlund went to work on the comet with such perseverance and success that in 1909 he was awarded the gold
medal of the Royal Astronomical Society. After his death
in 1916 the Pulkovo Observatory continued to issue predictions for the return of Encke's comet, with which this
institution has been concerned for a century. (They probably feel as if they own it by now.) The comet continues to
show slight deviations from its predicted position occasionally, but not of the uniform type it exhibited in Encke's
time. The hypothesis of a resisting medium is no longer
regarded with favor. It seems more reasonable to attribute
the accelerations in its motion to the observations themselves. There are reasons for believing that the comet's
center of mass does not coincide with its center of light.
Measures on its position would lead to an apparent acceleration in the comet's motion, depending upon whether the
displacement is toward or away from the sun. Other possibilities are the accumulation of slight errors in the calculation of the perturbations; or the disturbing action of
material ejected from the nucleus. Whatever it may be,
there is no reason to suspect the law of gravitation is at
fault.

## TO CONTACT A COMET

There is no lack of theoretically possible ways of sending
a probe from the earth to Encke's comet. The number

would seem to be limited only by the time available for computing them. In reality the number is severely restricted by practical considerations. Many routes otherwise desirable are automatically ruled out by energy considerations. The orbits demand more energy than can be obtained from any of the rocket fuels now available. Other critical factors are the time of transit, the distance between comet and earth at contact, and the date until the next opportunity for a launch. To set a date ten years ahead would necessitate too long a wait; whereas a date ten weeks ahead might not allow sufficient time for preparation.

The earth was exceptionally well situated with respect to Encke's comet at its apparition of May 1964. Out of several possible transfer orbits, earth to comet, we show one here that would have gotten the probe to its target in 115 days. Since this opportunity is past, it might seem that a description of contact at some future date would be desirable. What is desirable is not always practicable. The public labors under the mistaken notion that all scientists have an electronic computer at their beck and call. The considerable amount of computing that this writer made for contact with the comet in 1964 was done with a table of logarithms, essentially the same method that Encke used 150 years ago. The method is still valid—but slow. In any event, it really doesn't matter whether the time is past or future, the principles involved are the same.

The circumstances of the encounter are shown in Figure 68. Launch is scheduled for March 17, 1964, when Encke's comet is 2.05 AU, or 191 million miles, from the earth, and 1.42 AU (132 million miles) from the sun. The orbital velocity of the probe twenty days after launch is 17.5 miles per second, and since it is approaching aphe-

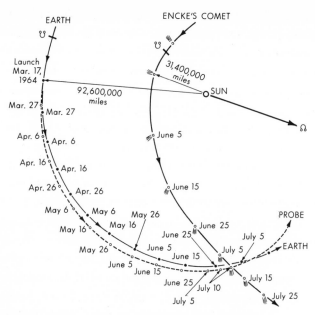

FIGURE 68. Path of probe on a dry paper run to Encke's comet. This projected run would bring the probe to within a distance of about 6 million miles at closest approach to comet. More trials would have to be made until satisfactory probe orbit is obtained.

lion is slowing down, dropping to 17.0 miles by July 10. As the earth is moving steadily at 18.5 miles per second, the probe soon is lagging far behind.

The orbital velocity of the comet at launch on March 17 is 18.1 miles per second. But as it is approaching the sun its velocity mounts rapidly, until at perihelion it reaches 43.2 miles per second. The probe is closest to the comet on July 10, when their distance apart is 0.071 AU, or about 6 million miles. This is missing by far too much, and slight adjustments would have to be made in the orbit of the probe until the separation was reduced to a satisfactory value.

Although in the diagram the probe looks as if it were dangerously close to the earth, there is never any chance of collision, as the earth is always well in advance. It must be remembered, too, that both probe and comet are *below* the plane of the earth's orbit, and not as close as they appear in the diagram. To fix the idea, you can think of Encke's comet as nosing below the plane of the diagram when it reaches the descending node of its orbit on May 25, like a porpoise diving under water. The probe goes underground immediately.

Another means of securing information on a comet has been suggested that does not require such an exacting schedule as the intercept experiment. So far, all our thinking has been concentrated on sending instruments to the comet, commanding them to obtain information and transmitting it back to earth. Although the operation is under control from the earth, this control is limited, and if serious trouble develops the whole mission may fail. But suppose we did the experiment the other way around? We keep the complex recording equipment on the earth, where it can be readily repaired if necessary. THEN . . . we proceed to stimulate the "observable characteristics of the comet."

How does one go about stimulating a comet?

We would still have to send a probe to the comet. But instead of being equipped with a mass of complex instrumentation, it would merely carry a nuclear weapon that could be detonated on command at the proper time. The results of the interaction between comet and bomb plasma would be observed and recorded on earth. Following such an explosion, the cometary material would become a powerful source of artificially created photon emission. Measures on these emissions should yield information on the chemical composition of the comet, as well as the abundance of elements in the nucleus and coma. Interaction between bomb plasma and cometary material would provide data on magnetic fields associated with the comet. Any radio emissions at cyclotron frequencies could be measured with radio telescopes and made to give additional information on atom densities, temperatures, and magnetic-field strengths.

A vital question is how long the effects produced by exploding a contaminant near a comet would last. If the observable effects were all over in a flash, the experiment would be of no value even if the bomb exploded squarely on the nucleus. Estimates indicate that 50 pounds of contaminant would produce effects that could be observed for five days. This is much longer than we could get information from a probe that would be within observing range of the comet for only a few hours. (Mariner II transmitted all the data about Venus in thirty-five minutes. The twenty-two photographs of Mars were taken by Mariner IV in twenty-four minutes.)

Public reaction to this bomb-comet experiment varies widely. Some people think we ought to give it a try. Others are shocked at the idea of blowing up an innocent little comet that never did any harm to anyone. Converting Encke's comet into a mass of bomb plasma seems to them as bad as shooting a faithful old horse and selling it to a glue factory.

CHAPTER 23

# Comet Ikeya-Seki:
# the great comet of 1965

On the morning of September 19, Tokyo Standard Time, two energetic amateur comet hunters, Kaoru Ikeya and Tsutomu Seki, independently discovered a nearly naked-eye comet that somehow had escaped detection until within scarcely an astronomical unit of the sun. "Object diffuse with a central condensation or nucleus and no tail," so the first dispatch read. This diffuse object was another "sun grazer," destined within about a month to pass 307,000 miles from the solar surface and become probably the brightest comet since the "great" comet of 1882. Like its famous counterpart of the last century, Ikeya-Seki was a conspicuous naked-eye object to many people in the southwestern part of the United States when it passed the perihelion of its orbit about noon on October 20. Those who failed to see the comet in the daytime due to clouds had an opportunity to view it later in the morning sky, when

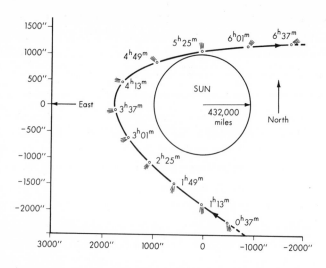

FIGURE 69. Apparent path of Comet Ikeya-Seki at perihelion passage on October 21, 1965, about 4 hours UT. This is path of comet as seen projected against the sky. At perihelion the comet was within 307,000 miles of the sun's surface. (Diagram from L. E. Cunningham, University of California, Berkeley.)

its slender curved tail, about the length of the handle of the Big Dipper, appeared above the eastern horizon a couple of hours before the sun. (Fig. 69)

Comet Ikeya-Seki (1965f) was moving in an essentially parabolic orbit and hence will never be seen again. But that does not necessarily mean that we will never see another bright comet moving in its orbit again. Not the *same* comet, of course, but a *different* comet moving in the *same* orbit. Such comets are said to be members of a *comet group*. They should not be confused with a comet "family," which as we have seen is something altogether different. About sixty-six comet groups have been tentatively identified, of which there are fifteen that can be regarded as well-established and designated by letters from A to Q. Comet Ikeya-Seki proved to be a member of the M group, the famous sun-grazing comets, which is the largest of the lot with eight, and possibly ten, members identified at the latest count. The members of this group so far as known are listed in Table 8. Doubtless there are other fainter ones that we have missed. Information is not available for two faint members.

We see that several other comets have approached considerably closer to the sun than Ikeya-Seki. These figures

T A B L E  8

## The Members of the M Group

| Comet (Year and name) | Apparent magnitude | Distance from solar surface at perihelion (miles) |
|---|---|---|
| 1668 | Bright | 5,760,000 |
| 1702 (?) | Faint | ? |
| 1843 I | Very bright | 79,000 |
| 1880 I | Much fainter | 79,000 |
| 1882 (?) | Faint | ? |
| 1882 II | Very bright | 283,000 |
| 1887 I | Much fainter | 469,000 |
| 1945 VII | Faint | 153,000 |
| 1963e (Pereyra) | Faint | 60,000 |
| 1965f (Ikeya-Seki) | Very bright | 307,000 |

should not be taken as absolutely fixed and unalterable, however, as their reliability can be no better than the observations upon which they are based. To fix the idea in mind, you can think of these comets as they come by as if they were different trains running on the same track and always in the same direction. It is impossible to buy a round-trip ticket on this line. You stand at the station (earth) watching the trains as they sweep past and wondering how many more there are up the track.

### CONFIDENTIAL: WHERE TO LOOK FOR A COMET

The hard part about comet hunting is that comets may show up anywhere. We know both when and where to look for a short-period comet, of course. (As a working definition, you can consider a "short-period" comet to be one that returns in less than 200 years.) Aside from some fifty short-period comets seen at more than one return, however, we have no way of knowing where a new, unexpected comet will put in its appearance.

Now we have no way of foretelling *when* the next member of the M Group will pay us a visit. But at least we have some general notion of *where* it should appear. For we already know the elements of its orbit quite accurately: they are the same as those of 1882 II and Ikeya-Seki. Therefore this next M member, when it comes, will be approaching the sun from approximately the direction of the aphelion of these two bright comets, in the northern part of Canis Major. This will be roughly its direction if

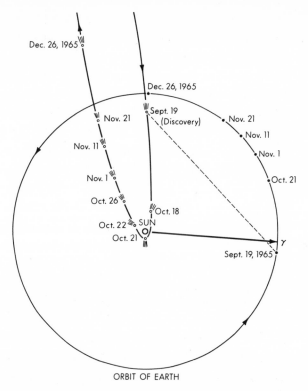

Dec. 26, 1965

Dec. 26, 1965

Sept. 19
(Discovery)

Nov. 21

Nov. 21

Nov. 11

Nov. 11

Nov. 1

Nov. 1

Oct. 21

Oct. 26

Oct. 18

Oct. 22 — SUN

Oct. 21

γ

Sept. 19, 1965

ORBIT OF EARTH

FIGURE 70. The orbit of Comet Ikeya-Seki projected onto orbit of the earth. Practically all the
comet's orbit is below plane of paper as indicated
by broken line. Comet was discovered on Sept. 19,
1965, when about 150 million miles from earth.

*far away.* When close, of course, it may lie in almost any
direction, depending upon where the earth happens to be
at the time.

Hence, if you are a comet hunter, it would be a good
idea to sweep around the Big Dog and outlying precincts

whenever possible. Comet Ikeya-Seki was magnitude 8 when discovered in Hydra, 30 degrees east of its aphelion position. (Fig. 70, p. 245)


WHAT THE COMET CONTAINED

Attempts to obtain spectra of Comet Ikeya-Seki were made not only from ground-based observatories, but from airplanes and rockets as well. Of course, this was not the first time that astronomers have gone aloft to observe a comet. Readers will remember that 1882 II was observed above the clouds from a balloon. Several spectra were secured at various observatories over the world, all of which reported that Ikeya-Seki showed a spectrum more like that of a meteor than a comet. The usual bright cometary emissions due to molecules were missing. In their place were many atomic lines due to metals, among those identified being sodium, iron, potassium, nickel, copper, and calcium. The absence of molecular emissions is not surprising. It is hardly to be expected that molecules—combinations of atoms—would be able to hold together so close to the sun. The terrific heat pouring from the solar surface less than a million miles away would tear apart all except the most firmly bound molecular compounds.

The most welcome discoveries in science are those that are unexpected. Observations of Comet Ikeya-Seki made with the radio telescope of the California Institute of Technology have revealed the presence of an enormous and previously unsuspected amount of radiation in the invisible infrared region of its spectrum. No immediate explanation was forthcoming, although some speculate the cause may be due to friction with solar protons, while others are inclined to believe it more likely that atomic processes are involved. Ikeya-Seki is the first comet ever examined for heat emission, and it will be extremely interesting to see if others are "hot" too.

## THE SUN AND A COMET IN COLLISION

So far as I am aware, the earliest *rational* attempt to account for the maintenance of the sun's heat was the meteoritic-infall hypothesis advanced in 1848 by J. Robert Mayer. He pointed out that space is known to contain innumerable small bodies, many of which must be drawn into the sun with speed approaching the parabolic velocity. As they plunge into the sun, their energy of motion would be converted into heat.

The idea sounded plausible and for a few years enjoyed considerable success. The trouble with the hypothesis was that it was too easily checked against observations. For an elementary calculation shows that if meteorites were bombarding the sun in sufficient quantity to keep it shining at its present rate, the earth should be blazing hot, too. But we can still use the principle involved to estimate the heat that would be released by a giant comet striking the sun. All we need to know are its mass and velocity at impact.

The mass of even the biggest of comets, as we have seen, must be insignificant compared with bodies such as the planets. Therefore, when we assume our comet has a mass of $1/1,000,000$ that of the earth, we are assuming plenty of comet.

We don't need to guess at the velocity. The nucleus

would encounter the solar surface with a velocity of 383 miles per second. The energy generated by such a mass at this velocity would be $1.134 \times 10^{37}$ ergs.

Now the sun is radiating energy continuously over its WHOLE SURFACE at the rate of $3.78 \times 10^{33}$ ergs per second. From the arithmetic it appears that the energy produced by collision with the comet would equal the total energy radiated by the sun in fifty minutes.

This is quite a sizable quantity of heat. Its effect upon the earth would depend upon how the encounter took place: whether the comet hit the sun on the near side or far side, and how fast the energy was released. My guess is that it would be released very quickly—in a minute or two—but others disagree. If it were all released in a flash near the apparent center of the solar disk, the results could be most instructive.

### WHAT IS THE ORIGIN OF A COMET GROUP?

How does a comet group originate?

How does *any* comet originate? When we can't even explain the existence of a solitary comet, how can we account for them by the dozen? For those who must have an answer, we offer the following:

We know from direct observation that comets occasionally split apart. The classic example is Biela's comet, which in January 1846, for reason or reasons known only to itself, underwent a kind of fission process, the two components continuing on their separate ways as complete and distinct comets. The pair returned as per schedule in 1852, although farther apart by a million miles. They passed out of observing range in September of that year, and were never seen again.

Consider a comet at the aphelion of its orbit situated about 40,000 AUs from the sun. Its period of revolution is 2,828,430 years. This primitive comet gives birth, or, if you prefer, undergoes disruption into a score or more comets of various sizes. These continue on, side by side, apparently moving in the same orbit as before. Yet the orbit is not *quite* the same. For if the orbit of the comet is a large one, such as we have postulated, the slightest change in velocity far from the sun will produce a significant change in the comet's period of revolution. Suppose after disruption at aphelion one component is speeding along at 0.00827345 miles per second, which in more familiar terms is about 30 miles per hour. Another component received a trifle extra impulse, causing it to move 0.00008273 miles per second faster. For a little while, perhaps 10,000 years, the distance between them increases very gradually. Nevertheless, one begins to lag behind, so much so that it passes perihelion twelve years after the other.

Hence, on the basis of the disruption hypothesis, a seemingly trivial difference in the velocities of the components of a comet would be amply sufficient to separate them by scores of years when they reach the vicinity of the sun. Yet all would file through the solar system in virtually identical orbits. A nice feature of the hypothesis is that there is no difficulty in accounting for the numerous members of Group M. All we need to do is to assume a big enough comet.

But why should a comet all alone, away out there in the cold of space, spontaneously break apart? That is a problem of a higher order of difficulty, to which we don't pretend to have an answer. But it is a good reason for giving each member of a comet group our closest attention.

# CHAPTER 24

## *"Call it Icarus"*

The discovery of Neptune is an old familiar story. We all know how Adams, a student at Cambridge University, England, calculated the position of the unknown body that was pulling Uranus out of its orbit. And how he sent his results to Airy, the Astronomer Royal, with instructions where to look for it. For some unknown reason Airy delayed a year before starting the search. In the meantime, Leverrier in France was working independently on the same problem. He wrote to the Berlin Observatory requesting that they search in the place directed. Galle and d'Arrest at Berlin did as instructed and found the planet in less than an hour.

It is not my purpose here to discuss the pros and cons of this famous case. The facts have been recorded for all to read. Yet in so many respects I still don't know *what happened*. Why did it take Airy so long to start rolling?

How was everything at home between him and Mrs. Airy?
Why didn't Adams look for Neptune himself? There was
a telescope on the campus at Cambridge. He might have
been able to recognize the planet by its disk. It would have
been worth a try anyhow. What did Galle and d'Arrest do
after they found Neptune? Did they shake hands and call
it a night? Or did they do a little celebrating down at the
village tavern? History is silent on these important questions.

These thoughts came to me while reading a publica-
tion by the Astronomical Society of the Pacific entitled
*Icarus and the Space Age.** Icarus is one of the 1600+
asteroids that have been officially named and numbered.
Asteroids are easy to discover. As we have said, it is hard
for a man who does much direct photography *not* to discover an asteroid. Asteroids have gotten to be such common objects that often astronomers don't bother to report
a new one any more.

UNLESS it happens to be an asteroid like Icarus. For
Icarus is our unique and most valuable asteroid. You can
be sure that in the years to come Icarus is going to be
accorded plenty of TLC.**

Icarus was discovered accidentally by Dr. Walter
Baade in 1949. The preliminary orbit of Object Baade was
computed by Dr. Seth B. Nicholson and myself. The little
body resorted to every trick in the business to get away
from us. The fact that it can never escape us now is due
to the skill and persistence with which Nicholson pursued
it.

Baade and Nicholson are both gone now. I would like

* Maud W. Makemson, Leaflet No. 397, July 1962.
** Tender Loving Care.

to tell about the capture of Icarus while I still have the details in mind. I wrote a brief semi-technical article on Icarus shortly after its discovery was announced. Now I would like to describe the search more fully than before, including not only the facts, but the human-interest side of the story that never got into the official formal reports.

On the night of June 26, 1949, Baade was working at the 48-inch Schmidt telescope on Palomar Mountain. One of the plates on his program was a sixty-minute exposure in the Scorpius region near Antares. A Schmidt telescope is not so much a telescope as a camera. You can't "look through" a Schmidt. With a Schmidt you can photograph a large area of the sky and get the stars in sharp focus clear out to the edge of the plate. Baade delayed developing his plates until after lunch next day, when he would have plenty of time. I never heard what he was after that night. Certainly it wasn't asteroids.

When he got around to developing his photograph of the Antares region he found this asteroid trail. It would have been impossible for him to have missed it. In eleven hours the trail would have covered a distance equal to the apparent diameter of the full moon. Motion as rapid as this indicates the object must be very close to the earth. The trail looked so interesting that Baade decided to get the two additional observations needed for an orbit. But where should he point his telescope?

A single asteroid trail is like an arrow without a head. The trail shows the *line* of motion but not the *direction*. From his one exposure he knew how far the asteroid moved in an hour. Hence he could estimate the distance it had covered a couple of days later when he wanted to shoot for it again. But should he shoot to the east or west of its present position? He guessed west and guessed right. How did he know?

Consider the motion of a planet such as Mars, whose orbit lies outside the orbit of the earth. Both planets are moving in the same direction in their orbits but the earth is moving the faster. Although Mars is moving steadily forward (eastward), as the earth gains upon it the planet seems to reach a stationary point relative to the stars. Then, as the earth passes it, Mars appears to move backward toward the west, or to *retrograde*. The date when earth passes Mars is known as *opposition*, because at this time Mars is seen in the *opposite* direction from the sun. Shortly after opposition Mars comes to a stop again at its *second* stationary point. As the earth moves on ahead, Mars resumes its eastward motion. The same remarks apply to other planets revolving in orbits beyond the earth, such as Jupiter and Saturn. You experience a similar effect in relative motion when you pass a slower-moving car on the freeway. Play that you are a computer and store in your memory that part about stationary points.

Since Baade had picked up the asteroid a little past opposition, it was a good bet that it was retrograding, or moving westward. So on June 28, when he took his second exposure, he set off the motion to the southwest of the object's position on the twenty-sixth. And sure enough, there it was. (Of course, if it hadn't been there he could have set off the motion to the northeast and taken another plate.) Now it was an easy matter to get the third observation on June 30. Thus, when he returned to the office of the Mount Wilson Observatory in Pasadena he had the minimum number of observations necessary to compute a preliminary orbit. Now all he had to do was to find somebody to compute it.

You might ask, why didn't Baade compute the orbit himself? The answer is that he had had no experience in orbit computation. He had never computed an orbit in his life. I asked him about this one day. He said the only time he had tackled the orbit of an asteroid he got an eccentricity greater than 1, which meant it was hyperbolic. This is ridiculous, since asteroids don't move in hyperbolic orbits. Baade said it made him so mad he never tackled an orbit again. (Three years later at the meeting of the International Astronomical Society in Rome, Baade read a paper that led astronomers to double the size of the universe. But he was baffled by the asteroids!) Another reason why he felt no inclination for the job was the fact that he was just about to leave on his vacation.

The most likely candidates for an orbit project were Nicholson and myself. At an institution such as the Mount Wilson and Palomar Observatories, the staff consists of astrophysicists dedicated to the proposition that the only things worth investigating are such way-out objects as the gaseous nebulae, star clusters, galaxies, etc. But Nicholson still retained a keen interest in the minor bodies of space. When a graduate student at the Lick Observatory, he had discovered the ninth satellite of Jupiter, J IX, in 1914; and in 1938 he had found J X and J XI at Mount Wilson. (Two years later he was to discover J XII, which put him even with Galileo at four moons apiece.) I had gained experience in this field helping Nicholson keep track of his satellites, which were always getting themselves lost. So Baade left his plates with us and promptly got out of town.

Before we could do anything on the orbit of the asteroid, we first had to get its position off the plates. This is done by measuring its distance from stars around it whose positions are already known. The coordinates of these comparison stars are recorded in catalogues issued by various observatories over the world. In 1887 astronomers started a project called the *Carte du Ciel* for mapping the sky, which was supposed to be finished in five or ten years. They're still working on it. As one astronomer remarked back in 1922, the *Carte du Ciel* is now "considerably overdue."

If a star catalogue is available for the zone you want, the work of measuring positions goes pretty fast. Object Baade was in the zone of $-28°$. The catalogues were in the library right where they should be for zones $-27°$ and $-29°$, and for some time we went confidently ahead looking for $-28°$. Then gradually the light began to dawn: *there was no zone* $-28°$.

As a result, Nicholson and I had to form astrographic positions for the stars around the asteroid by hooking them up with stars on the zones adjacent. Besides taking time, it forced us to determine positions for the asteroid from star positions that were themselves of low accuracy. We got an unexpected setback the first time we tried to put one of our plates on the measuring machine. It was no go. The machine had never been designed to take a $14 \times 14$-inch plate. It would have been easy to make the plate fit by cutting it, but this we hesitated to do. There is always the risk that instead of *cutting* a plate you will *break* it. (There was no diamond-point glass cutter available then.) As everyone knows, you can do a marvelous job of slicing up a worthless plate. But try one that is precious and you lose your nerve, with disastrous results.

We evaded the difficulty in a cowardly way by making positive contact prints of the region around the asteroid and measuring them. This again impaired the accuracy of the positions. These were minor problems that would have been of no consequence if we had not been so pressed for time. But this was a case when time was very much of the essence. Other asteroids, such as Apollo, Adonis, and Hermes, had been found with remarkable orbits, and were now hopelessly lost for lack of observations. Object Baade would surely suffer a similar fate unless we could get an orbit for it in a hurry.

Four days were spent in identifying the comparison stars, measuring the plates, and performing the reductions on our raw measures. By Saturday, July 9, however, we had three beautiful values for the right ascension and declination of Object Baade, all corrected and reduced to the equator and equinox of 1950.0. It was a proud moment when we finally airmailed these to the Harvard College Observatory, which acts as the clearinghouse for astronomical discoveries. Harvard would now send our positions to observatories in the United States and Canada on Announcement Cards. Astronomers who were interested could go to work on the orbit and (we hoped) secure some more observations of the object itself.

Nicholson used to say that there is more work involved in getting three observations of an object than in computing its orbit. Orbit people may not agree, but that is because they probably have never taken an observation in their lives. Once you have the observations in the proper form, determining the orbit from them is a comparatively straightforward process. At a certain stage in the Laplacian method, which we were using, you can check the accuracy of your orbit by seeing how closely it will reproduce the observations upon which it is based. If the observed and computed positions are not in satisfactory agreement, then they must be made to agree. This is done by performing an operation upon the orbit called a *differential correction*. It sounds like a desperation procedure analogous to an exploratory laparotomy in surgery. Most orbits require a differential correction as a matter of routine. A preliminary orbit is imperfect, not because of errors in computation, but because the observations and the orbit method itself are imperfect.

✓ Most of the hot Sunday of July 10 went into grinding away on the differential correction. We had transferred our base of operations to the lowest floor of the office, since it was the coolest place in the building. Although we hadn't computed the elements yet, the work was getting more exciting at every step, as it was becoming quite evident that we had latched on to a most exceptional asteroid. The differential correction was successful, so we could go ahead on the ephemeris. I remember sitting out on the front steps of my home that evening, watching the stars come out over the deodar trees and feeling well pleased with the world in general and myself in particular.

This fatuous state of optimism was of brief duration. Now a new threat began to rear its ugly head—the moon. Object Baade had found a powerful ally in our satellite, which had gotten around into the Scorpius region and was blotting out the stars with its effulgent rays. A photograph of the asteroid would be fogged so badly as to be quite useless. Maybe in a few days, when the moon was farther away, we would be able to pick up the object on a short exposure.

Nicholson and I usually computed together so we could check occasionally for numerical errors. But as Seth was busy on some other job next day, I went ahead on my own. Since the differential correction had come out all right, I decided to compute the elements. The six elements enable you for the first time to form a mental picture of the orbit in space. The element that defines the size of the orbit is *a*, the length of the semi-major axis, expressed in astronomical units (AU). You can think of the astronomical unit as the mean distance of the earth from the sun of 93 million miles; that is, 1 AU = 93 million miles.* There are only two bodies in the solar system which have semi-major axes of less than 1. These are Venus with $a = 0.723$, and Mercury with $a = 0.387$.

In our formula, the semi-major axis is obtained from its reciprocal, $1/a$. Since I had to take the reciprocal of a number greater than 1, I could see in advance what the result was going to be. Yet I could hardly believe my eyes as the machine turned the numbers up on the dial: 9 . . . 5 . . . 8 . . . 6 . . . 9. Object Baade had a semi-major axis of 0.95869 AU—the first object ever *discovered* with a semi-major axis less than unity.

We had imposed upon one of the members of the staff, Bruce Rule, to try for some photographs of the asteroid. He was on the program at the 48-inch Schmidt beginning Tuesday night. To reach Palomar Mountain by noon it is necessary to be on the bus that leaves Pasadena at seven in the morning. We had hoped to have an ephemeris done by Monday evening, but as usual it took longer than we

---

* This is a very loose way of describing the astronomical unit. Rigorously, it must be defined through Kepler's third law and the Gauss constant, k.

anticipated. (An ephemeris is a series of positions of an object at equal intervals apart—say, every four days or eight days, depending upon circumstances.) But we had it finished by afternoon so we were able to give it to Rule over the telephone on Palomar. He said he would do the best he could for us, but the moon was still uncomfortably close, and he couldn't make any promises.

While awaiting news from Palomar, we received a disquieting letter from Leland E. Cunningham of the University of California at Berkeley. Readers may recall that Cunningham was the discoverer of the bright comet (1940d) that bears his name. Cunningham had been doing some figuring with our three positions on the Harvard Announcement Card. According to his calculations, the three positions could be represented about equally well by half a dozen orbits, with semi-major axes ranging all the way from 0.9 AU to infinity! In other words, our orbit was virtually *indeterminate,* and therefore practically useless for prediction purposes unless improved by more observations. But how could we get more observations if we didn't know where to point our telescope? We seemed to be trying to buck Murphy's law, which asserts that everything that can go wrong will go wrong.

But then we got a break. Rule was successful in photographing the region (presumably) occupied by the asteroid on July 12 and 13. As he knew how anxious we were to see the plates, he went to the trouble of bringing them directly over as soon as he was back in Pasadena. He showed up still wearing the old clothes that astronomers wear when working at the telescope, and although he must have looked like a bum to some people, he certainly looked good to us. We were jubilant, for we were sure that Object

Baade must be somewhere on the broad expanse of those 14 × 14 plates.

But finding the asteroid this time was quite a different proposition than it had been three weeks earlier. On the discovery plates the asteroid was retrograding rapidly and left a long trail among the stars. Now the asteroid had found an ally in the *earth*. For it had reached its second stationary point—remember?—so that its motion relative to the stars was scarcely perceptible. To make matters worse, it had gotten into a particularly rich section of the Milky Way, a regular star cloud. Among the hundreds of thousands, or maybe millions, of star images, how were we ever going to locate the particular image we wanted?

The situation was not quite so hopeless as it sounds, as we didn't have to search every one of the 196 square inches on a plate. What we did was to calculate the particular square inch where the asteroid *should* be. If our orbit was any good at all, we should be able to hit it within an area of a square inch. Then our problem was to find an image elongated just enough to distinguish it from the circular star images.

It was no trouble at all to find suspicious-looking images. The area was positively teeming with asteroids—except that upon closer scrutiny they turned out to be defects in the emulsion. After a couple of days devoted to tracking down Eastman asteroids, we couldn't help feeling some anxiety. Besides looking for an elongated image, we also tried another method of search using the blink comparator. With this device two plates are adjusted separately until the star images on them match when viewed in the eyepiece. The plates are examined alternately by switching rapidly back and forth from one to the other.

The star images remain stationary. But if an object is moving, its image on one plate will not quite match with its image on the other. Thus an asteroid will reveal itself by the way it "blinks" or "jumps" back and forth among the star images. But unfortunately for us, the images obstinately refused to "blink."

I always regard this as the critical point in the investigation—the time when success hung in the balance, as the saying goes. For if we couldn't uncover the asteroid within a few days, we might as well give up and admit it had us licked. I was feeling real low when I came back from lunch one afternoon and found Nicholson in my office. He calmly announced that he had found the object. He had been optimistic before over some hopeful-looking image, but this time he was very confident. Identification was confirmed beyond doubt when our measures showed the images on the two plates were separated by just the calculated amount.

The new positions enabled us to derive an improved orbit that revealed its true character. It was somewhat of a blow when the semi-major axis turned out to be 1.066 instead of 0.959, but we managed to bear up. The path of the object was more like that of a comet than an asteroid. At perihelion it goes inside the orbit of Mercury to within about 17 million miles of the sun. At aphelion it goes beyond the orbit of Mars out to about 183 million miles from the sun. The climate on Object Baade would certainly not be lacking in variety. At the far end of the orbit a man would be in a state of deep freeze. Then 204 days later he would be incinerated. The maximum temperature of an airless nonrotating black planet distant 17 million miles from the sun is 527° C. The actual temperature must be below this figure. If above about 450° C., however, the asteroid would glow a dull red.

How big is Object Baade? We can only guess. The asteroid does not show a disk even in the largest telescopes. Therefore we cannot determine its size in the usual way by measuring its apparent diameter. The only way we can get at its diameter is by making some sort of assumption about the reflecting properties of its surface, or its *albedo*. It seems reasonable to suppose that an asteroid would have a low albedo of, say, 0.06, about the same as that of the moon and Mercury. As a matter of self-education I have calculated the diameter of the asteroid on the basis of several slightly different assumptions. Being as generous as possible, I make it about 1.1 miles in diameter, or 6000 feet.

After we had gotten the asteroid safely under control, the next big problem was what to name it. In response to our request, we received letters from R. C. Cameron of Indiana University and Dr. G. E. Folkman of Clemenon, Michigan, both of whom suggested the name "Icarus." In classic mythology, Daedalus and his son Icarus were imprisoned by King Minos on the isle of Crete. The king kept a close watch on all ships, so that they were unable to escape by sea. Daedalus outwitted the king by making huge wings for himself and Icarus, which he attached to their shoulders with wax. After cautioning his son not to fly too high lest the heat of the sun melt the wax, they set out over the Aegean Sea. But Icarus paid no heed to his father's words, and promptly took off for outer space. Under the increasing heat of the sun the wax began to melt, his wings came loose, and he plunged to his death in the sea.

Icarus sounded like an excellent choice to me, but of course the decision rested entirely with Baade. Of the three of us, he had always seemed the least concerned over the fate of the asteroid. Baade had an abrupt, staccato way of talking that could be rather disconcerting until you got to know him better. He gave the letters a hasty glance, as if finding a suitable name was to him a matter of complete indifference. "All right, call it Icarus," he barked. "Then any more asteroids like it will be members of the Icarus group." And it was so ordered.

## ICARUS AND VULCAN

As soon as the orbit was announced, it occurred to several people that Icarus might be the elusive planet Vulcan, over which there was so much controversy in the last century. So far as I am aware, the first person to raise this question was the late Dr. E. T. Bell, a professor of mathematics at the California Institute of Technology in Pasadena. Dr. Bell was better known as "John Taine," the name under which he wrote many stories and novels of science fiction.

Vulcan was supposed to be a planet revolving so close to the sun that it was only observable at a total solar eclipse or when in transit. From some transit observations, Leverrier became convinced of the reality of Vulcan, and announced that it revolved around the sun in a period of 19.75 days at a distance of 13 million miles. But as repeated attempts to find Vulcan ended in failure, the belief in its existence gradually died out. (At the total eclipse of July 29, 1878, astronomers claimed to have sighted four unknown bodies. Because so many Vulcans turned up, people refused to believe in the reality of any of them.)

The orbit of Icarus bears but scant resemblance to the orbit that Leverrier deduced for Vulcan. Nevertheless, it is possible for Icarus to transit the sun. This can only occur if Icarus is at its ascending node on or about December 21. The "ascending node" is the point where a planet crosses the plane of the earth's orbit from south to north. The "descending node" is the point where it crosses the plane of the earth's orbit from north to south. Notice that we didn't say "it is possible for Icarus *to be seen* to transit the sun." For Icarus would be 70 million miles from the earth when in transit and, if only a mile in diameter, would be quite invisible. A transit at the descending node is impossible, as Icarus is then seen in the OPPOSITE direction of the sun from the earth.

### 1968: ARIA DA CAPO

In 1968, the earth, Mercury, and Icarus will be going through the same roles that they played nineteen years earlier when the asteroid was discovered. A little figuring will show that nineteen revolutions of the earth are approximately equal to seventeen revolutions of Icarus and seventy-nine revolutions of Mercury, as may be seen from this table:

| Object | Period | | |
|--------|--------|---|---|
| Earth | 1.00 years | × 19 = | 19.00 years |
| Icarus | 1.12 " | × 17 = | 19.05 |
| Mercury | 0.24 " | × 79 = | 19.02 |

It is evident that wherever earth, Icarus, and Mercury may be in their orbits NOW, they were at very nearly the same positions nineteen years earlier, and they will return to these same positions nineteen years hence. Thus, just as in 1949, on May 1, 1968, Icarus will pass within 8 million miles of Mercury. Later, on June 15, the asteroid will come within 4 million miles of the earth.

## NUMBER 1566 VALUABLE TEST BODY

It would be a tragedy if a space ship should collide with 1566, the official number assigned to Icarus. For 1566 is a very valuable asteroid. We must be careful not to damage it.

The general theory of relativity predicts that the orbit of a planet does not remain fixed in space, but undergoes a slow rotation in the direction of the planet's motion. The rate of revolution is greatest for small orbits of high eccentricity. The effect amounts to 43″ per century for Mercury, and is in exact agreement with observation. Mercury was the only body available for this test until the discovery of Icarus. Although the effect for Icarus is only about one-fourth of that for Mercury, the asteroid will eventually become a better test body than the planet, owing to the larger eccentricity of its orbit. Unfortunately, observations over possibly a century will probably be required before the relativity advance in the perihelion of Icarus can be determined with confidence.

Another method by which we might be able to observe a general relativity effect in the motion of Icarus within only a few years was first pointed out in 1965 by Mary Parmenter Francis. Although mathematicians have long been aware of this effect, they disregarded it as being far below the limits of observation. But modern developments in technology have changed all that.

Besides the advance in the perihelion of Icarus, there is also a relativity change in the radius of the orbit. The effect consists of a general shrinkage in size, which at a distance of 1 AU amounts to 31 miles. At the close approach of June 1968 of about 4 million miles, the shrinkage in the orbit would cause a displacement in the apparent position of Icarus of 1″.4. Whether large radars can track a body only about 1 mile in diameter, such as Icarus, is a question. If such a feat is possible, it would be a most important observation to make, inasmuch as it would provide an independent check on the relativity advance of the perihelion.

Oh, yes, I almost forgot! Walter Baade, besides discovering Icarus, the asteroid that comes nearest the sun, also discovered Hidalgo (944), the asteroid that goes farthest from the sun. Another of his asteroids is 966, Muschi, which was a pet name for his wife. Quite a record—in addition to doubling the size of the universe!

*Appendices*

# Locating stars by right ascension and declination

This subject is set apart from the rest of the book as one impossible to present in an easy, descriptive fashion. It is also a subject of basic importance in astronomy, knowledge that everyone who aspires to astronomy must have. Here we give enough of the bare essentials to enable a person to set an equatorial telescope on a star, and find his way around the heavens.

In Chapter 13 we described a method of locating an object on the celestial sphere, such as a fireball, by two coordinates called altitude and azimuth. We began by defining two fundamental reference points, the zenith directly overhead, and the nadir directly underfoot. Midway between them we drew an imaginary circle called the astronomical horizon. Angular distance measured vertically upward from the horizon to an object we called altitude. Its direction in the sky, or azimuth, gave us more trouble. We had to pick out a particular direction arbitrarily from which to measure azimuth. The one usually chosen is the vertical circle that passes through the observer's zenith and the north and south points on the horizon, called the *meridian*. Distances measured from the north point to the right, or east, define an object's azimuth.

This method of fixing position by the horizon system has its merits but it also has some serious defects. Each person in a sense carries his own zenith and horizon around with him, so that the altitude and azimuth of a star for an observer in Los Angeles is different from the same star seen at the same time by an observer in San Francisco. Also, since the stars are continuously moving across the sky from east to west, their altitudes and azimuths are continually changing. Plainly, to advance we need a reference system for celestial objects that is good for any observer, anywhere, at any time.

## THE EQUATOR SYSTEM

We can devise such a system by proceeding in the same general way as we did with the horizon system. We begin with the two imaginary points where the axis of the earth, prolonged indefinitely, would pierce the celestial sphere. These points we call the north and south celestial poles. Polaris is within about a degree, or two full moons, of the north celestial pole. There is not even a moderately bright star near the south celestial pole, or a "South Star." Midway between the celestial poles we draw an imaginary circle called the celestial equator. If you were at the equator of the earth, and if the celestial equator were drawn across the heavens with luminous paint, you would see it arching directly over your head, dividing the northern half of the sky from the southern half.

Now imagine circles drawn from pole to pole crossing the celestial equator at right angles. These circles we call *hour circles*, for reasons that will appear later. (In a planetarium you can see these circles projected onto the sky, so you don't have to imagine them.) We can have as many of these hour circles as we like, so that there is one passing through every star in the heavens. To find the angular distance of a star north or south of the celestial equator, we start at the celestial equator and measure along its hour circle until we come to the star. The angular distance so measured is the star's *declination*. If the star is north of the celestial equator, its declination is marked + or N; the declination of stars south of the equator are marked − or S. The symbol for declination is the Greek small letter delta, $\delta$.

A little thought will show that if a star is on the equator its declination must be $0°$. If the star were at the north celestial pole its declination would be $90°$. (For Polaris, $\delta = 89° \, 01'$.) The famous constellation of Crux, the Southern Cross, is centered at about $\delta = -70°$.

Having rather easily disposed of distances north and south of the equator, we are now confronted with the problem of how to measure in an east-west direction. Since all the hour circles look alike, we have to select one arbitrarily as our zero hour circle, somewhat as the meridian through Greenwich, England, is the prime meridian for measuring longitude on the earth. Astronomers define the hour circle of $0^h$ as the one that goes through the vernal equinox, the point already described where the sun crosses the celestial equator from south to north each year about March 21.

Angular distance measured from the vernal equinox

eastward along the celestial equator to the hour circle passing through the star is called its right ascension. East in the sky is in the opposite direction to the daily motion of the stars parallel to the celestial equator. Right ascension is denoted by the Greek small letter $\alpha$.

Since the day is divided into twenty-four hours, and since the celestial sphere completes one rotation through 360° every twenty-four hours, one hour of right ascension corresponds to $360°/24 = 15°$. (It would simplify astronomical calculations if we denoted right ascension by degrees only, instead of hours, minutes, and seconds of time, but we have been chained to it so long we can't break away from it now.) Starting at the vernal equinox, we mark the hour circle through it $0^h$. Then continuing eastward along the celestial equator for 15°, we mark the hour circle there $1^h$; the hour circle through 30° we mark $2^h$, and so on through 360°, when we come back to the vernal equinox at $24^h$, or $0^h$, again.

Suppose the hour circle of $10^h$ is on your meridian. It moves on to the west and an hour later is replaced by the hour circle through $11^h$. The hour circle of $10^h$ is now $1^h$ to the west of the meridian. After another hour, the hour circle of $12^h$ is on the meridian and the hour circle of $10^h$ is $2^h$ west of the meridian. Or we say it has an *hour angle* of $2^h$. Hour angle is counted westward from the meridian along the celestial equator to the hour circle passing through the star, on up to $24^h$, or $0^h$. Since it is rather awkward to talk of hour angles exceeding $12^h$, we often find it convenient to speak of negative hour angles or hour angles east. Thus, a star with an hour angle of $22^h$ west can be considered as having an hour angle of $-2^h$, or $2^h$ *east*.

Some evening you notice that the bright star Sirius is on, or very nearly on, your meridian. You look up Sirius in a star catalogue and find its right ascension is $6^h$ $43^m$. This tells you immediately that the right ascension of your meridian is also $6^h$ $43^m$, the same as that of Sirius. Next summer you see Vega crossing your meridian one evening. According to the catalogue, the right ascension of Vega is $18^h$ $35^m$. Therefore, the right ascension of your meridian is $18^h$ $35^m$. By memorizing the right ascensions of various stars distributed around the sky, and noticing when they are on or near your meridian, you would be able to estimate the particular section of the celestial sphere that was overhead at any time.

But after a while you would say to yourself, "Why bother to run outdoors and try to find one of my key stars? Why not use a clock to keep track of the stars? The celestial sphere turns at a steady rate. When Sirius is on the meridian I set a clock to read $6^h$ $43^m$. My clock runs at the same rate as the celestial sphere. Then just by glancing at the clock I can always tell which hour circle is on my meridian, even when the sky is covered with clouds."

Clocks of this kind are standard equipment in all large observatories. They are called *sidereal* clocks because they show sidereal, or *star*, time. Ordinary clocks like your wristwatch are rated to keep time adjusted to the sun, or mean solar time. Owing to the daily apparent eastward motion of the sun, a day by your wristwatch is about four minutes (3 minutes 56.55536 seconds) longer than a day measured by the stars. Therefore, a sidereal clock is rated faster than an ordinary clock, and is always gaining on it. If you visit an observatory, don't try to set your watch by their sidereal timepiece.

## HOW TO FIND YOUR SIDEREAL TIME

Now we are going to give you a quick, easy way of finding the approximate sidereal time for any hour of any date.

On March 21 we know the sun is at the vernal equinox and its right ascension is $0^h$. Each day the sun moves eastward or increases its right ascension by very nearly $4^m$. After fifteen days it will have increased its right ascension by $15 \times 4^m = 60^m$, or $1^h$, and in a month by about $2^h$. Thus, with a little mental arithmetic you can reckon the right ascension of the sun by counting the months and days since March 21. For example, on June 21, which is three months after the vernal equinox, the right ascension of the sun is $6^h$; on September 21 the right ascension of the sun is $12^h$, etc. On September 25, or four days after the twenty-first, the right ascension of the sun would be $12^h\ 16^m$, approximately.

Your wristwatch reads, say, 5:10 P.M. some afternoon. This means that the hour angle of the sun is about $5^h\ 10^m$ over in the west. So what is the sidereal time? Let us say the date is June 21, when the right ascension of the sun is $6^h$. Count from the sun $5^h\ 10^m$ to the east along the celestial equator until you come to the meridian. Its right ascension, or the sidereal time, must be $6^h\ 00^m + 5^h\ 10^m = 11^h\ 10^m$. Thus with the aid of an ordinary pocket watch you can find the sidereal time closely enough for identifying stars.

## SIDEREAL TIME AND THE TELESCOPE

Most small telescopes are mounted on a stand like a photographer's camera, so that they can be turned right or left and up and down. Such a mounting is all right for a photographer when taking a picture of some fixed object like a mountain or building. But it doesn't work so well for observing stars with a telescope. For, owing to the rotation of the earth, the stars are always moving to the west. They keep drifting out of your field of view, forcing you to keep moving the telescope every few seconds along with them.

This apparent motion of the stars can be overcome by a telescope mounted equatorially and made to turn by a clock or motor at the same angular rate as the stars. (Naturally, it will cost you more money, too.) An equatorial telescope is mounted on two axes at right angles to each other. One, called the polar axis, is set parallel to the axis of the earth at your station. The other axis is the "declination" axis. The clock-drive turns the telescope westward on the polar axis at the same rate as the stars. If in good adjustment, it will hold a star nearly fixed in the field of view instead of having it always drifting out of your sight.

There are two ways to set an equatorially mounted telescope. One is by the same method you would use on a telescope mounted over the back of a chair: by sighting along the tube until you see what you are aiming at. But suppose you want to see the planet Neptune. You can't pick up Neptune by sighting along the tube. So you have to resort to the setting circles.

First set the declination circle until it reads the same as the declination of Neptune. You will find the position of Neptune given by a book published each year at the U.S. Naval Observatory called *The American Ephemeris and Nautical Almanac*. When the circle is set for the declination of Neptune that night, clamp it in position. (But be sure the telescope isn't aimed north of the equator when it should be south, or vice versa.)

According to the *Ephemeris*, let's say, the right ascension of Neptune is $15^h$ $11^m$. Your sidereal clock reads $16^h$ $21^m$, which means that at the moment Neptune is

$$16^h\,21^m - 15^h\,11^m = 1^h\,10^m$$

to the west of your meridian. So you set the hour circle to read $1^h$ $10^m$ in hour angle west. (It is a good idea to calculate the hour angle about five minutes ahead to give you time to make your setting.) Now you clamp the telescope in hour angle, so it begins tracking the stars, and look hopefully into the eyepiece. (Always use a low power when making a setting.) If Neptune is not in sight, move the telescope around the region with slow motions. It may be just out of the field of view. But if you fail to pick it up after a persistent search, you had better check your settings over again to be sure you haven't slipped up somewhere (like using last year's *American Ephemeris*, for instance).

## STARS AND STAR CHARTS

The constellations are most readily identified from charts which show only stars easily visible to the eye. Although under favorable conditions the eye can see stars as faint as sixth magnitude, the charts included here show only stars down to the fourth magnitude, which are bright enough to catch your attention quickly. When beginning, a star chart that shows too much detail is a hindrance rather than a help. This writer went through the painful process of learning the constellations at the age of twelve from charts on which the stars were enmeshed in a tangled background of mythological figures: dragons, sea monsters, club-wielding giants, damsels in distress, etc. Start with constellations you can't fail to recognize, like the Big Dipper and the stars that form the W in Cassiopeia, and work from them. If possible, try to find someone who already knows the constellations and ask him over some night. In the course of the evening you might suggest that you step outside and have a look at the stars. Once you learn some key constellations and bright stars, you will have no trouble locating the fainter ones.

HOW TO USE THE CHARTS

The best way to learn to use the star charts is by some examples.

The date is August 21. It is nine o'clock in the evening by standard time. What stars will be overhead and where will you find them on the charts?

First find the approximate sidereal time. Since August 21 is five months after March 21, the right ascension of the sun is about $5 \times 2^h = 10^h$. At nine o'clock in the evening the hour angle of the sun is $9^h$. Counting eastward from the sun $9^h$ the sidereal time is:

Right ascension of meridian = right ascension of sun + hour angle of sun = $10^h + 9^h = 19^h$, approx.

Where does this put us on the star maps?

Look at Map 2. Right ascension is marked at the top and bottom of the map. Notice that, contrary to the usual custom, the numbers increase to the left instead of right. Declination is indicated at right and left on the sides of the chart, counting to the north and south from the celestial equator drawn horizontally across the center.

We see from Map 2 that $19^h$ right ascension lies near three first-magnitude stars: Deneb, Altair, and Vega, which form what is known as the "summer triangle." Constellations with larger right ascensions than $19^h$ will be in the east, rising and approaching your meridian. Constellations with smaller right ascensions will be moving from the meridian and setting. Thus you see at a glance that Pegasus, at about $23^h$ $30^m$ is $4^h$ $30^m$ east of the meridian, rising low in the east; but Cygnus, at about $20^h$ $30^m$, is well-placed for observation nearly overhead. Boötes, at $15^h$, is $4^h$ west of the meridian, already rather low in the sky. Low in the southwest we make out the winding line of stars that mark the Scorpion, one of the few constellations that bears a slight resemblance to the object after which it was named.

Here is another example, which is about as difficult as any that is likely to come up.

The date this time is January 27. The time is six o'clock in the morning.

January 21 is only two months before March 21, when the right ascension of the sun will be $24^h$. In these two months the sun will move $2 \times 2^h = 4^h$ of right ascension, which in this case we will subtract from $24^h$, making the right ascension of the sun $20^h$ on January 21. Since it is the morning of January 27 the sun has gone on another six days, or $6 \times 4^m = 24^m$, in right ascension. The right ascension of the sun is therefore $20^h$ $24^m$, approximately.

Now at midnight the hour angle of the sun was $12^h$ west, and since then it has gone on another six hours, making its hour angle $18^h$. Adding this on to the right ascension of the sun, we go eastward until we come to the meridian at $20^h$ $24^m + 18^h$ $00^m = 38^h$ $24^m$. We get rid of the excess hours by subtracting $24^h$, making the sidereal time about $14^h$ $24^m$. In this case it would have been easier to regard the hour angle of the sun as $- 6^h$ or $6^h$ east and subtracted, giving the sidereal time as $20^h$ $24^m - 6^h$ $00^m = 14^h$ $24^m$, the same as before.

We find right ascension $14^h$ $24^m$ on Map 4, crossing the sky near the bright orange star Arcturus. Another bright star, Spica, will be about $1^h$ west of the meridian in the south, and Antares also in the south about $2^h$ east. These are stars we are used to seeing in the evening during July and August—which shows that by getting up early enough in the winter you will be able to see the stars of summer.

Of course, a star map can be used the other way around to obtain an estimate of the right ascension and declination of an object. Suppose you have discovered a possible comet which is at about the center of the square in Pegasus. In-spection of Map 2 shows that the center of the square of Pegasus is at about $\alpha = 23^h$ $40^m$, $\delta = +22°$. This then is also the approximate position of your comet.

## TO CHANGE TO UNIVERSAL TIME (UT)

The universal time (UT) corresponding to the me-ridian through Greenwich, England, is found in the United States by adding the difference in longitude, as follows:

Eastern Standard Time (EST) $+ 5^h$ $= UT$
Central Standard Time (CST) $+ 6^h$ $= UT$
Mountain Standard Time (MST) $+ 7^h = UT$
Pacific Standard Time (PST) $+ 8^h$ $= UT$

Instead of designating time before noon as A.M., and time after noon as P.M., it is more convenient to count time from midnight ($00^h\ 00^m$) through $24^h$. Thus 3:00 P.M. becomes $15^h\ 00^m$.

Examples: The time in New York is Jan. 24, $05^h\ 20^m$ EST.

$$UT = 05^h\ 20^m + 5^h = 10^h\ 20^m \text{ of Jan. 24 UT.}$$

The time in Los Angeles is March 3, $17^h\ 41^m$, PST.

$$UT = 17^h\ 41^m + 8^h = 25^h\ 41^m.$$

Since this is more than $24^h$, the date is one day later at Greenwich, so that the UT is $01^h\ 41^m$ of March 4.

If you are on Daylight Saving Time remember to subtract $1^h$ from your watch time, then proceed as usual.

The following star maps are from *The Fascinating World of Astronomy* by Robert S. Richardson, McGraw-Hill.

# STAR MAPS

Map 1  North Circumpolar Stars
Map 2  Fall and Winter Stars
Map 3  Winter and Spring Stars
Map 4  Spring and Summer Stars

## MAP 1

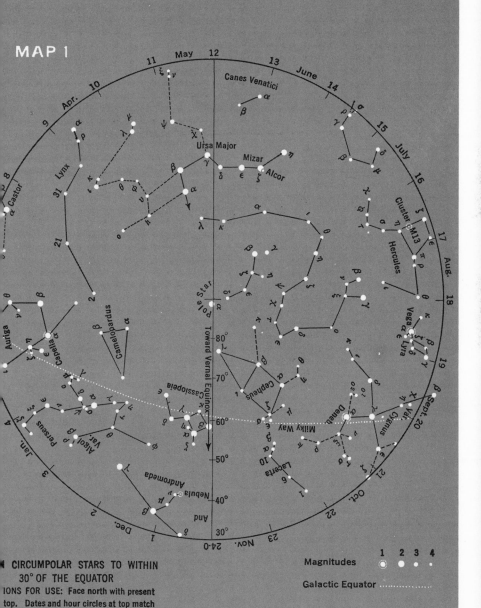

◄ CIRCUMPOLAR STARS TO WITHIN
30° OF THE EQUATOR

IONS FOR USE: Face north with present
top.  Dates and hour circles at top match
n north side of the mercator maps.

Magnitudes

1  2  3  4

Galactic Equator ..............

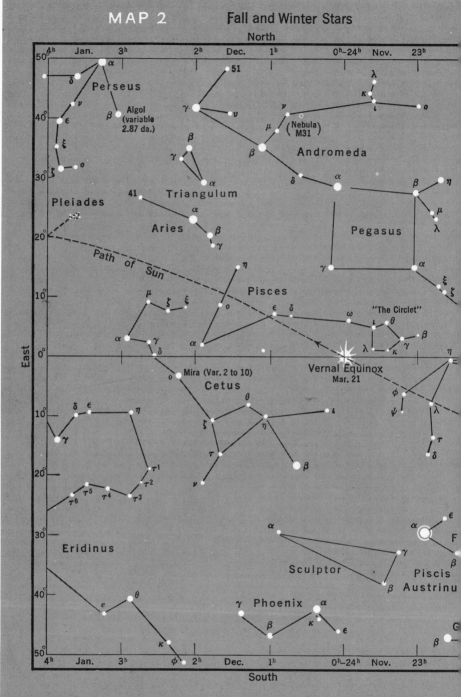

# MAP 2     Fall and Winter Stars

**North**

**East**

Perseus

Algol (variable 2.87 da.)

Pleiades

41

Triangulum

Aries

Path of Sun

Pisces

Andromeda

(Nebula) M31

Pegasus

"The Circlet"

Vernal Equinox Mar. 21

Mira (Var. 2 to 10)

Cetus

Eridinus

Sculptor

Piscis Austrinu

Phoenix

F

G

**South**

Jan.   4ʰ   3ʰ   2ʰ   Dec.   1ʰ   0ʰ–24ʰ   Nov.   23ʰ

**DIRECTIONS:**

In whichever direction you are looking, hold that edge of the map down. Then raise it above the head if you wish.
The months given at top and bottom of map indicate approximately when these stars are near the meridian at about
To extend view northward match hour circles (or months) given at edge of these maps with the upper ones of the pol

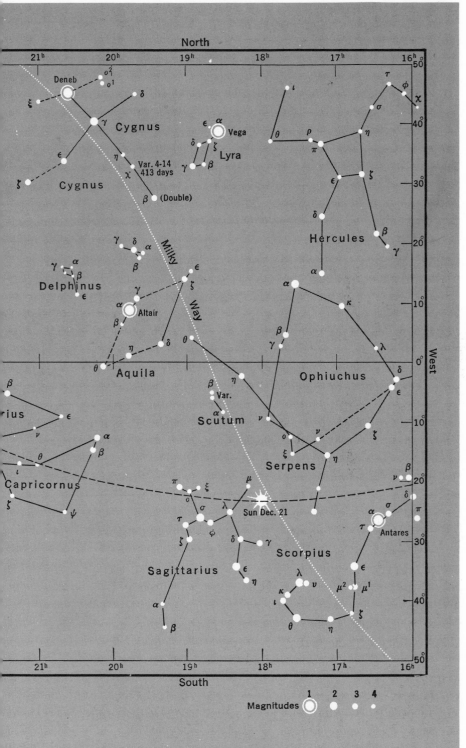

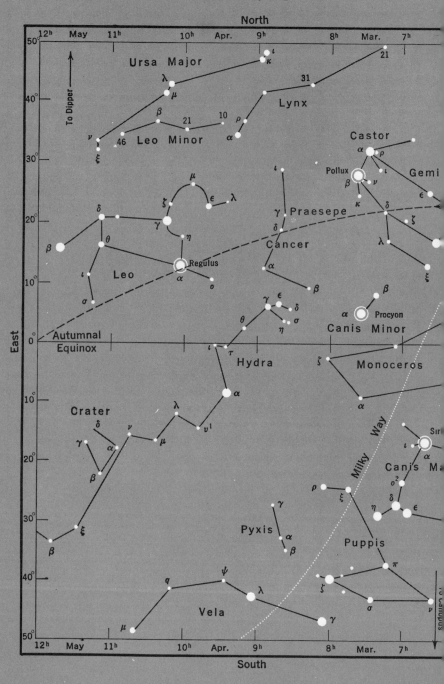

# MAP 3    Winter and Spring Stars

North

South

East

Autumnal Equinox

To Dipper

**Ursa Major**

**Lynx**

**Leo Minor**

**Leo**

Regulus

**Cancer**

Praesepe

Castor

Pollux

**Gemi**

Procyon

**Canis Minor**

**Monoceros**

**Hydra**

**Crater**

**Pyxis**

**Puppis**

**Canis Ma**

Siri

Milky Way

**Vela**

(SEE MAP 2 FOR DIRECTIONS)

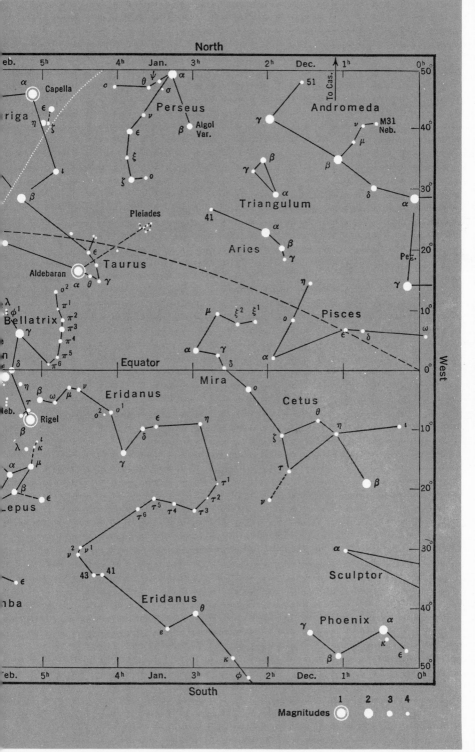

# MAP 4    Spring and Summer Stars

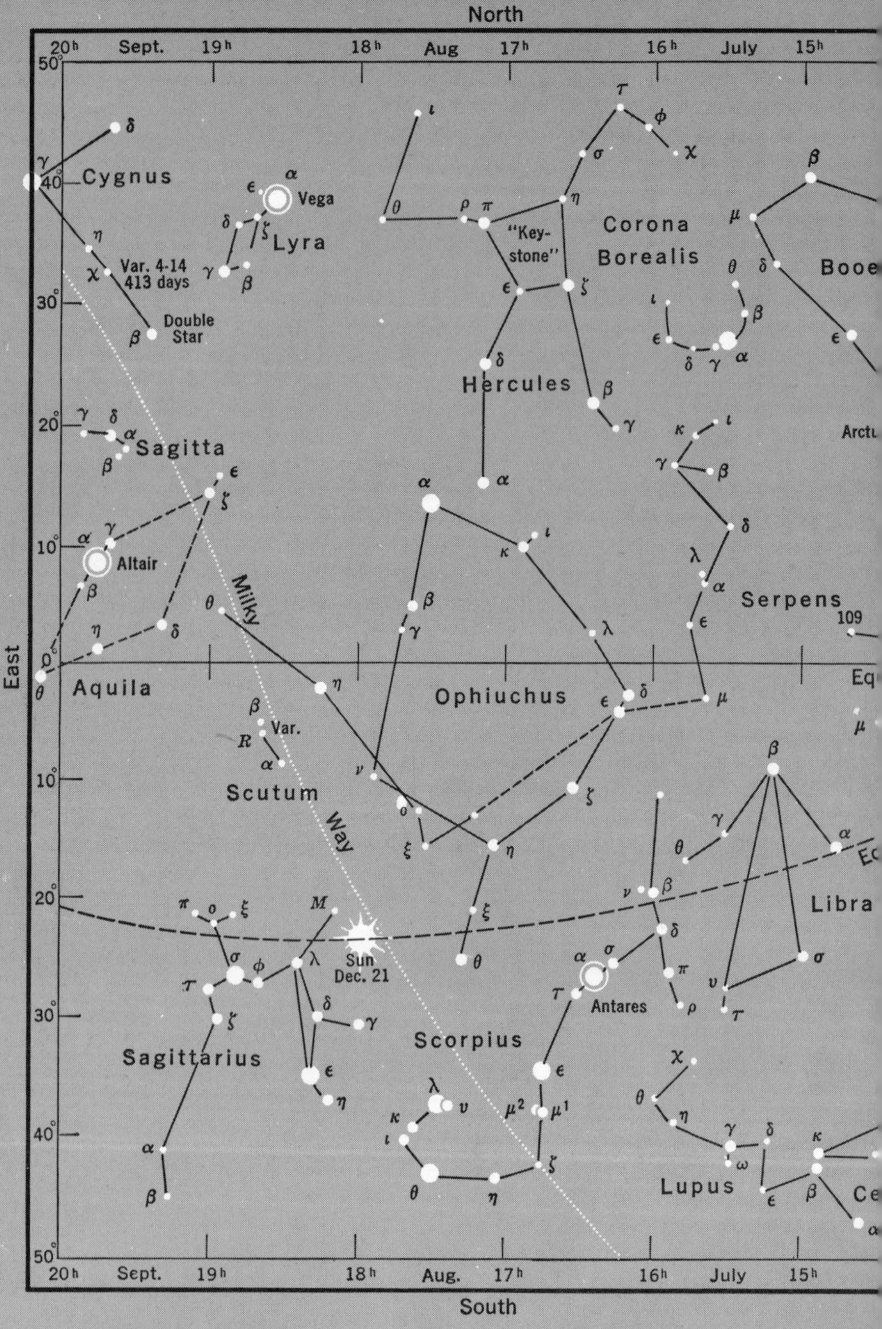

**North**

20ʰ   Sept.   19ʰ     18ʰ   Aug.   17ʰ     16ʰ   July   15ʰ

50°

δ

γ
40° **Cygnus**

ι

ε  α Vega

τ
σ  φ
χ

φ

β

**Corona
Borealis**

μ

**Booe**

η
χ     Var. 4-14
413 days
β   Double
Star

δ
δ  ζ
**Lyra**
γ
β

30°

θ  ρ π
η

"Key-
stone"

ε   ζ

δ

**Hercules**

β

γ

θ  δ

ι
ε
δ  γ  α
β

κ   ι

**Booe**

ε

Arct

γ
δ
α
β
λ
δ
ε
α
ε
**Serpens**
109

**Eq**

γ  δ
20°   α
β   **Sagitta**

ε

α  γ
10°     ζ
α   Altair
β

α        α
β
γ

κ  ι
λ
μ

η      δ
0°  ε         θ
θ   **Aquila**

η

ε

δ  μ

μ

**East**

**Ophiuchus**

β
R  Var.
α
**Scutum**

ν

ζ

10°

π o  ξ
σ
τ   φ
ζ

o
ξ

M
λ

η

ξ

θ

β

γ

θ
ν  β
δ

α

**Libra**

σ

20°

Sun
Dec. 21

δ
γ

ε
η

λ
κ  ν
ι

θ

α  σ
τ   Antares

ε
μ²  μ¹

π
ν  ρ
τ

σ

**EC**

**Sagittarius**

**Scorpius**

α

χ
θ  η  γ  δ

κ

30°

θ     η

ζ

ω
ε

**Lupus**

β   Ce

40°

β

50°

20ʰ   Sept.   19ʰ     18ʰ   Aug.   17ʰ     16ʰ   July   15ʰ

**South**

(SEE MAP 2 FOR DIRECTIONS)

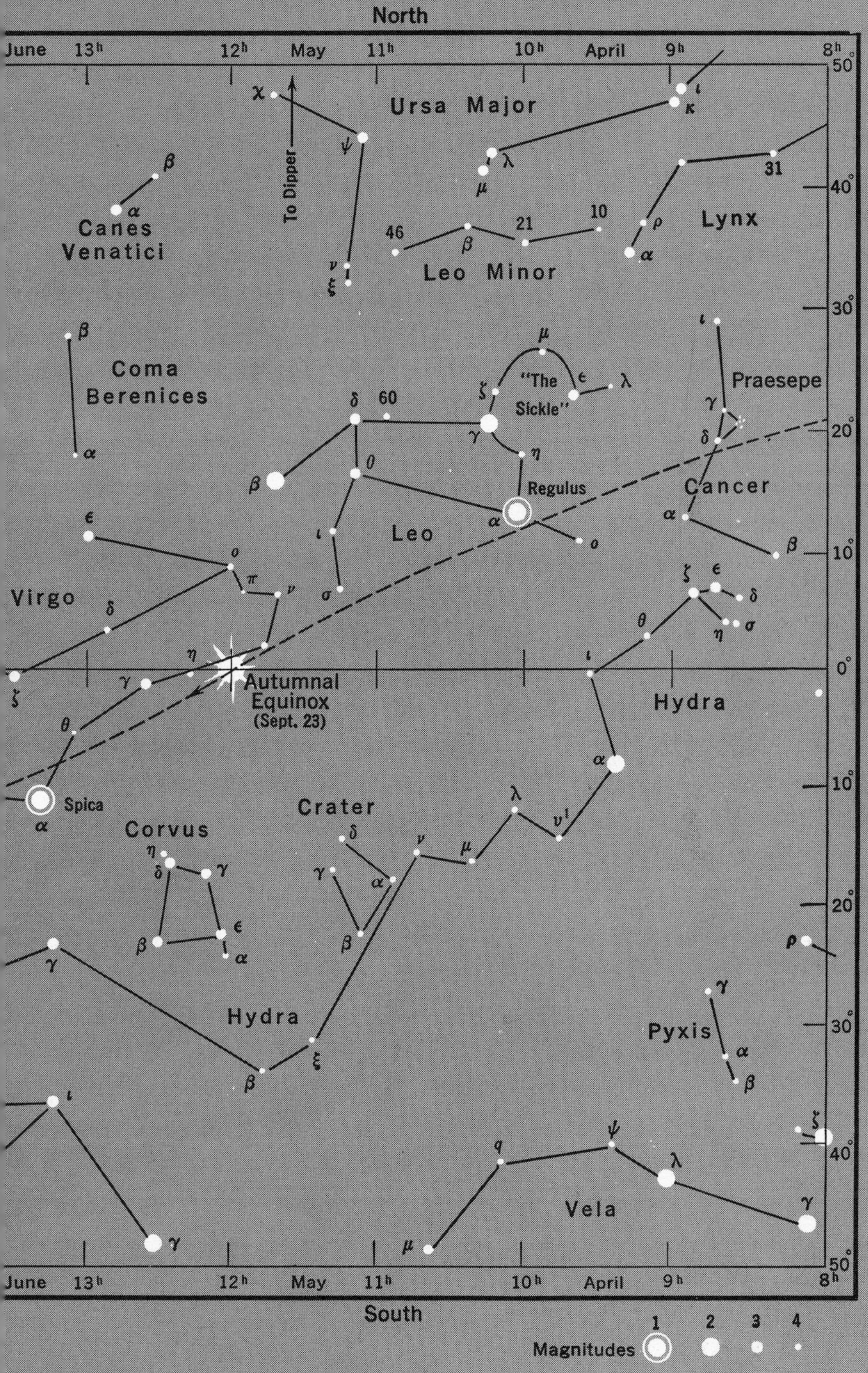
North
June
13h
12h
May
11h
10h
April
9h
8h
Ursa Major
To Dipper
Canes Venatici
Leo Minor
46
21
10
31
Lynx
Coma Berenices
"The Sickle"
60
Praesepe
Regulus
Cancer
Leo
Virgo
Autumnal Equinox (Sept. 23)
Hydra
Spica
Crater
Corvus
Hydra
Pyxis
Vela
South
West
50°
40°
30°
20°
10°
0°
10°
20°
30°
40°
50°
Magnitudes
1
2
3
4

| Comet | Semi-major axis a (AU) | Perihelion distance q (AU) | Aphelion distance Q (AU) | Eccentricity e | Argument of perihelion ω |
|---|---|---|---|---|---|
| Encke | 2.21 | 0.339 | 4.09 | 0.847 | 185°2 |
| Grigg-Skjellerup | 2.87 | 0.850 | 4.89 | 0.704 | 356.3 |
| Honda-Mrkos-Pajdusakova | 3.01 | 0.556 | 5.46 | 0.815 | 184.1 |
| Tempel (2) | 3.02 | 1.369 | 4.68 | 0.548 | 191.0 |
| Tuttle-Giacobini-Kresak | 3.11 | 1.117 | 5.10 | 0.641 | 37.9 |
| Pons-Winnecke | 3.35 | 1.161 | 5.54 | 0.653 | 170.2 |
| Kopff | 3.42 | 1.516 | 5.32 | 0.556 | 161.7 |
| Giacobini-Zinner | 3.45 | 0.936 | 5.97 | 0.729 | 172.8 |
| Perrine-Mrkos | 3.47 | 1.154 | 5.78 | 0.667 | 167.8 |
| Wolf-Harrington | 3.49 | 1.604 | 5.37 | 0.540 | 187.0 |
| Schwassmann-Wachmann (2) | 3.49 | 2.157 | 4.83 | 0.383 | 357.7 |
| Daniel | 3.54 | 1.465 | 5.62 | 0.586 | 7.3 |
| Wirtanen | 3.54 | 1.618 | 5.47 | 0.543 | 343.5 |
| D'Arrest | 3.55 | 1.378 | 5.73 | 0.612 | 174.4 |
| Arend-Rigaux | 3.56 | 1.385 | 5.73 | 0.611 | 326.4 |

# Short-period comets of more than one appearance*

| Longitude of ascending node $\Omega$ | Inclination from ecliptic $i$ | Period of most recent orbit $P$ (Years) | Time of recent perihelion passage $T_1$ | Approximate time of later perihelion passages | |
|---|---|---|---|---|---|
| | | | | $T_2$ | $T_3$ |
| 334°7 | 12°4 | 3.30 | 1964.42 | 1967 Sept. | 1971 Jan. |
| 215.4 | 17.6 | 4.90 | 1957.09 | 1971 Oct. | 1976 Sept. |
| 233.1 | 13.2 | 5.21 | 1954.10 | 1969 Sept. | 1974 Dec. |
| 119.3 | 12.5 | 5.27 | 1957.10 | 1967 Aug. | 1972 Nov. |
| 165.6 | 13.8 | 5.48 | 1951.35 | 1967 Oct. | 1973 April |
| 94.4 | 21.7 | 6.12 | 1951.69 | 1970 Jan. | 1976 Mar. |
| 121.0 | 4.7 | 6.32 | 1958.05 | 1970 Sept. | 1977 Jan. |
| 196.0 | 30.9 | 6.42 | 1959.82 | 1972 Aug. | 1979 Jan. |
| 242.6 | 15.9 | 6.47 | 1955.74 | 1968 Sept. | 1975 Feb. |
| 254.2 | 18.5 | 6.51 | 1958.61 | 1971 Aug. | 1978 Feb. |
| 126.0 | 3.7 | 6.53 | 1961.68 | 1968 Mar. | 1974 Oct. |
| 69.7 | 19.7 | 6.66 | 1950.64 | 1970 Aug. | 1977 April |
| 86.5 | 13.4 | 6.67 | 1961.29 | 1967 Dec. | 1974 Aug. |
| 143.6 | 18.1 | 6.70 | 1950.43 | 1970 July | 1977 Mar. |
| 124.6 | 17.2 | 6.71 | 1957.69 | 1971 Feb. | 1977 Oct. |

* Catalogue of Cometary Orbits, Memoirs of the British Astronomical Association, Vol. 39, No. 3, June, 1961.

SHORT-PERIOD COMETS OF MORE THAN ONE APPEARA

| Comet | Semi-major axis a (AU) | Perihelion distance q (AU) | Aphelion distance Q (AU) | Eccentricity e | Argument of perihelion ω |
|---|---|---|---|---|---|
| Reinmuth (2) | 3.56 | 1.933 | 5.18 | 0.457 | 45.5 |
| Brooks (2) | 3.56 | 1.763 | 5.36 | 0.505 | 197.1 |
| Harrington (2) | 3.59 | 1.582 | 5.60 | 0.559 | 232.8 |
| Johnson | 3.62 | 2.26 | 4.97 | 0.375 | 205.9 |
| Finlay | 3.62 | 1.077 | 6.17 | 0.703 | 321.6 |
| Borrelly | 3.67 | 1.452 | 5.88 | 0.604 | 350.8 |
| Faye | 3.80 | 1.652 | 5.95 | 0.565 | 200.6 |
| Whipple | 3.80 | 2.45 | 5.16 | 0.356 | 190.4 |
| Ashbrook-Jackson | 3.83 | 2.32 | 5.34 | 0.394 | 349.1 |
| Reinmuth (1) | 3.88 | 2.026 | 5.74 | 0.478 | 12.9 |
| Arend | 3.93 | 1.83 | 6.03 | 0.534 | 44.5 |
| Oterma | 3.96 | 3.39 | 4.53 | 0.144 | 354.9 |
| Schaumasse | 4.06 | 1.20 | 6.92 | 0.705 | 52.0 |
| Wolf (1) | 4.14 | 2.51 | 5.78 | 0.395 | 161.1 |
| Comas Solá | 4.20 | 1.78 | 6.61 | 0.576 | 40.0 |
| Väisälä | 4.78 | 1.74 | 7.82 | 0.636 | 44.4 |
| Neujmin (3) | 4.93 | 2.03 | 7.83 | 0.588 | 144.8 |
| Schwassmann-Wachmann (1) | 6.38 | 5.54 | 7.21 | 0.131 | 355.8 |
| Crommelin | 9.19 | 0.74 | 17.64 | 0.919 | 196.0 |
| Stephan-Oterma | 11.50 | 1.60 | 21.39 | 0.861 | 358.4 |
| Westphal | 15.62 | 1.25 | 29.98 | 0.920 | 57.1 |
| Brorsen-Metcalf | 16.83 | 0.48 | 33.18 | 0.971 | 129.5 |
| Olbers | 16.92 | 1.18 | 32.65 | 0.930 | 64.6 |
| Pons-Brooks | 17.12 | 0.77 | 33.47 | 0.955 | 199.0 |
| Halley | 17.95 | 0.59 | 35.31 | 0.967 | 111.7 |
| Herschel-Rigollet | 28.98 | 0.75 | 57.22 | 0.974 | 29.3 |
| Grigg-Mellish | 30.00 | 0.92 | 59.08 | 0.969 | 328.4 |

ONT. )

| Longitude of ascending node $\Omega$ | Inclination from ecliptic $i$ | Period of most recent orbit $P$ (Years) | Time of recent perihelion passage $T_1$ | Approximate time of later perihelion passages | |
|---|---|---|---|---|---|
| | | | | $T_2$ | $T_3$ |
| 296.2 | 7.0 | 6.71 | 1960.90 | 1967 Aug. | 1974 April |
| 176.9 | 5.6 | 6.72 | 1960.46 | 1967 Mar. | 1973 Nov. |
| 119.2 | 8.7 | 6.80 | 1960.49 | 1967 April | 1974 Feb. |
| 118.2 | 13.9 | 6.87 | 1956.56 | 1970 April | 1977 Mar. |
| 42.1 | 3.6 | 6.90 | 1960.67 | 1967 July | 1974 June |
| 76.2 | 31.1 | 7.02 | 1960.45 | 1967 June | 1974 |
| 206.3 | 10.6 | 7.41 | 1955.17 | 1969 Dec. | 1977 |
| 188.5 | 10.3 | 7.42 | 1955.91 | 1970 Oct. | 1978 |
| 2.3 | 12.5 | 7.51 | 1956.26 | 1971 April | 1978 |
| 123.6 | 8.4 | 7.65 | 1958.23 | 1973 July | 1981 |
| 357.6 | 21.7 | 7.79 | 1959.67 | 1967 June | 1975 |
| 155.1 | 4.0 | 7.88 | 1958.44 | 1974 Mar. | 1982 |
| 86.2 | 12.0 | 8.18 | 1960.29 | 1968 June | 1976 |
| 203.9 | 27.3 | 8.43 | 1959.22 | 1967 Aug. | 1976 |
| 62.8 | 13.4 | 8.59 | 1961.26 | 1969 Nov. | 1978 |
| 135.4 | 11.3 | 10.46 | 1960.35 | 1970 Oct. | 1981 |
| 156.2 | 3.8 | 10.95 | 1951.40 | 1973 April | 1984 |
| 321.6 | 9.5 | 16.10 | 1957.36 | 1973 June | |
| 250.4 | 28.9 | 27.87 | 1956.80 | 1984 Sept. | |
| 78.6 | 17.9 | 38.96 | 1942.96 | 1981 Dec. | |
| 347.3 | 40.9 | 61.73 | 1913.90 | 1975 | |
| 311.2 | 19.2 | 69.06 | 1919.79 | 1988 | |
| 85.4 | 44.6 | 69.57 | 1956.0 | 2025 | |
| 255.2 | 74.2 | 70.86 | 1954.39 | 2025 | |
| 57.8 | 162.2 | 76.03 | 1910.3 | 1986 | |
| 355.3 | 64.2 | 156.00 | 1939.60 | 2096 | |
| 189.8 | 109.8 | 164.30 | 1907.23 | 2071 | |

| Name | Approximate limits | Visibility |
|------|--------------------|------------|
| Quadrantids | Jan. 3–4 | Late morning |
| Lyrids | April 19–22 | Most of night |
| Eta Aquarids | May 3–4 | Morning |
| Perseids | July 27–Aug. 17 | After midnight |
| Orionids | Oct. 15–25 | After midnight |
| Leonids | Nov. 14–18 | Morning |
| Geminids | Dec. 9–14 | Most of night |

# Principal meteor showers

| Radiant R.A. | Dec. | Remarks | Associated comet |
|---|---|---|---|
| 15ʰ 20ᵐ | 49°N | Swift | |
| 18 04 | 34°N | Swift | 1861 I |
| 22 24 | 2°S | v. swift | Halley |
| 03 00 | 57°N | Swift | 1862 III |
| 06 16 | 16°N | v. swift | Halley |
| 10 08 | 22°N | v. swift | 1866 I |
| 07 28 | 32°N | med. swift | |

## HOURLY RATE *

| Altitude | Factor | Altitude | Factor |
|---|---|---|---|
| 0°0 | | 27.4 | |
| | 0.1 | | 0.6 |
| 2.6 | | 34.5 | |
| | 0.2 | | 0.7 |
| 8.6 | | 42.5 | |
| | 0.3 | | 0.8 |
| 14.5 | | 52.2 | |
| | 0.4 | | 0.9 |
| 20.7 | | 65.8 | |
| | 0.5 | | 1.0 |
| | | 90.0 | |

\* This table is based on a formula derived by J. P. M. Prentice. It shows clearly that it is useless to expect to see many meteors below an altitude of about 30°.

*Index*

# Index

Comets, Nagata, 4
nature of, 22–36
"new," 216
nucleus, 25, 34–36, 116, 117, 175, 180–184
origin, 210–224, 248
Oterma (P/), 38, 221
Pajdušáková 1953 h, 38
Peltier 1936 II, 38, 119, 121
Pereyra 1963 e, 184, 243
poison gases, 100
Pons (Encke) (P/), 39, 231–234
Pons-Brooke (P/), 215
probe, 225–240
resisting medium, 233–236
Ross (P/), 215
sand-bank model, 116–123, 171, 172, 228
Schwassmann-Wachmann (2), 39
Schwassmann-Wachmann (1), 125 II (P/), 38, 39, 72, 186–195
Seki-Lines 1962c, 115
spectra, 111–123
atomic, 113
Doppler shift, 115, 122
first photographed, 112
fluorescence, 121, 123
"forbidden lines," 114, 115
of Ikeya-Seki, 246, 247
molecular, 113
of P/1925 II, 195
"stimulating," 239, 240
"sun grazers," 28, 114, 184, 241
tails:
"anti-tails," 28, 30
development of, 28

Comets, tails, effect of solar radiation, 32, 33, 119–122
length, 28, 29
mass, 32–36
orientation, 31, 32
Tcherepashtshuk 1956d, 38
Tebbutt, 112
Tempel, 169
Tuttle (P/), 215
Väisälä 1959 I, 38
visibility, 23–25
Wilson-Harrington, 227
Wirtanen 1957 VI, 188, 193
Wolf (1) (P/), 118, 221, 223, 224
1528, 24
1668, 184, 243
1702, 243
1786, 232
1795, 232
1805, 232
1843 I, 184, 243
1862 III, 169, 170
1880 I, 184, 243
1881 VI, 64
1882, 243
1882 II, 39, 183–185, 243, 244, 246
1886 III, 212
1887 I, 243
1907 II, 14
1910 I, 41, 205
1945 VII, 184, 243
Constellations, 274–279
Aries, 88, 89
Big Dipper (Ursa Major), 57, 66, 126, 136, 137, 242
Boötes, 278

Robert S. Richardson was formerly on the staff of the Mount Wilson and Palomar Observatories and later Associate Director of the Griffith Observatory and Planetarium in Los Angeles. He received his B.A. degree from UCLA and his Ph.D. degree from the University of California at Berkeley. Richardson obtained experience in calculating orbits of comets and asteroids while working in association with Dr. Seth B. Nicholson, discoverer of four of the moons of Jupiter. Nicholson and Richardson computed the first orbit of the remarkable asteroid *Icarus*, which saved it from being lost. Richardson's books include *Exploring Mars, Man and the Planets,* two junior novels, *The Missing Men of Saturn* and *Second Satellite; Astronomy in Action, The Fascinating World of Astronomy,* and, with W. T. Skilling, *Sun, Moon and Stars.* Dr. Richardson lives in Altadena, California, with his wife and daughter and devotes his time entirely to writing.